C000194476

AQA GCSE (9–1)
English Literature

A Christmas Carol

David Grant

Published by Pearson Education Limited, 80 Strand, London, WC2R ORL.
www.pearsonschoolsandfecolleges.co.uk

Text © Pearson Education Ltd 2018
Produced and typeset by QBS Learning

The right of David Grant to be identified as author of this work has been asserted by him in accordance with the Copyright, Designs and Patents Act 1988.

First published 2018

21 20 19 18
10 9 8 7 6 5 4 3 2 1

British Library Cataloguing in Publication Data
A catalogue record for this book is available from the British Library

ISBN 978 1 292 25078 6

Printed in Slovakia by Neografia

Note from the publisher
Pearson has robust editorial processes, including answer and fact checks, to ensure the accuracy of the content in this publication, and every effort is made to ensure this publication is free of errors. We are, however, only human, and occasionally errors do occur. Pearson is not liable for any misunderstandings that arise as a result of errors in this publication, but it is our priority to ensure that the content is accurate. If you spot an error, please do contact us at resourcescorrections@pearson.com so we can make sure it is corrected.

Contents

1 Getting the plot straight

This unit will help you to understand and remember the plot of *A Christmas Carol*. The skills you will build are to:

- remember the sequence of key events in the novel
- understand the causes and consequences of the key events in the novel
- understand what makes some events in the novel more significant than others.

In the exam you will face questions like the one below. This is about the extract on the next page. At the end of the unit you will **plan your own response** to this question.

Exam-style question

Starting with this extract, how does Dickens present Scrooge as stubborn and heartless?

Write about:

- how Dickens presents Scrooge as stubborn and heartless in this extract
- how Dickens presents Scrooge as stubborn and heartless in the novel as a whole.

(30 marks)

Before you tackle the question you will work through three key questions in the **skills boosts** to help you to get the plot of *A Christmas Carol* straight.

 1 How do I make sure I know the plot?

 2 How can I explore the development of the plot?

 3 How do I know which are the most significant events in the novel?

Read the extract on the next page from Chapter 1 of *A Christmas Carol*.

As you read, think about the following:

Where in the novel does this extract appear? Is it near the beginning, in the middle or at the end?

What has happened before this extract? What happens after this extract?

In what ways does Dickens present Scrooge as stubborn and heartless in the extract?

Exam-style question

Read the following extract from Chapter 1 of *A Christmas Carol*.

In this extract Scrooge is visited by his nephew, Fred.

Extract A | Chapter 1 of *A Christmas Carol* by Charles Dickens

The door of Scrooge's counting-house was open that he might keep his eye upon his clerk, who in a dismal little cell beyond, a sort of tank, was copying letters. Scrooge had a very small fire, but the clerk's fire was so very much smaller that it looked like one coal. But he couldn't replenish it, for Scrooge kept the coal-box in his own room; and so surely as the clerk came in with the shovel, the master predicted that it would be necessary for them to part.

5 Wherefore the clerk put on his white comforter, and tried to warm himself at the candle; in which effort, not being a man of a strong imagination, he failed.

"A merry Christmas, uncle! God save you!" cried a cheerful voice. It was the voice of Scrooge's nephew, who came upon him so quickly that this was the first intimation he had of his approach.

"Bah!" said Scrooge, "Humbug!"

10 He had so heated himself with rapid walking in the fog and frost, this nephew of Scrooge's, that he was all in a glow; his face was ruddy and handsome; his eyes sparkled, and his breath smoked again.

"Christmas a humbug, uncle!" said Scrooge's nephew. "You don't mean that, I am sure."

"I do," said Scrooge. "Merry Christmas! What right have you to be merry? What reason have you to be merry? You're poor enough."

15 "Come, then," returned the nephew gaily. "What right have you to be dismal? What reason have you to be morose? You're rich enough."

Scrooge having no better answer ready on the spur of the moment, said, "Bah!" again; and followed it up with "Humbug."

"Don't be cross, uncle," said the nephew.

20 "What else can I be," returned the uncle, "when I live in such a world of fools as this? Merry Christmas! Out upon merry Christmas! What's Christmas time to you but a time for paying bills without money; a time for finding yourself a year older, and not an hour richer; a time for balancing your books and having every item in 'em through a round dozen of months presented dead against you? If I could work my will," said Scrooge, indignantly, "every idiot who goes about with 'Merry Christmas' on his lips, should be boiled with his own pudding, and buried with a

25 stake of holly through his heart. He should!"

How do I make sure I know the plot?

A *Christmas Carol* is written in five staves or chapters. Focus on the memorable key characters and events that appear in each chapter to make sure you know the novel's plot.

① The appearance of spirits, and the visions they show to Scrooge, are key events in the novel.

a How many spirits appear to Scrooge altogether? Circle Ⓐ the correct answer.

1	2	3	4	5

b In which chapter does each spirit appear? Add 🖉 the spirits to the plot summary below.

② **a** What happens at the beginning of the novel? Add 🖉 key events to the plot summary below.

b What happens at the end of the novel? Add 🖉 key events to the plot summary below.

Plot summary

Chapter 1	Chapter 2	Chapter 3	Chapter 4	Chapter 5

③ The reader is shown some characters in reality, and some in the visions that Scrooge is shown by the spirits.

a Label 🖉 all the characters in the list below with '**Pa**' if they are from Scrooge's past, '**Pr**' if they are from Scrooge's present, and '**F**' if they are in Scrooge's future.

b Add 🖉 each character, and any other details about what they do or say, to the correct chapters in the plot summary above.

> Some characters appear in the present, in visions of the present and in visions of the future. Check you have added these characters to every chapter in which they appear.

☐ **Ebenezer Scrooge**, a miserly businessman

☐ **Fred**, Scrooge's nephew

☐ **Fan**, Scrooge's sister and Fred's mother

☐ **Belle**, Scrooge's former fiancée

☐ **Fezziwig**, Scrooge's former employer

☐ **Bob Cratchit**, Scrooge's employee

☐ **Tiny Tim Cratchit**, their young, disabled son

☐ **The Cratchit family**, Bob's wife and other children

☐ **A group of businessmen**, discussing a man's death

☐ **A group of poor people**, planning to sell a dead man's belongings

☐ **The Ghost of Christmas Past**

☐ **The Ghost of Christmas Present**

☐ **The Ghost of Christmas Yet To Come**

☐ **Jacob Marley**, Scrooge's former business partner

☐ **Ignorance and Want**, two children shown to Scrooge in a vision

② How can I explore the development of the plot?

The plot of *A Christmas Carol* follows the change in Scrooge from miserable and miserly to happy and generous. Each key event shows either **why** Scrooge decides to change, or **how much** he has changed.

① Look at some of the key events in the plot of *A Christmas Carol*.

Chapter 1

Scrooge is mean to his employee, Bob Cratchit.

Scrooge is mean to his nephew, Fred.

Scrooge is mean to a man collecting for charity.

Scrooge is visited by the Ghost of Jacob Marley.

Chapter 2

Scrooge is visited by the Ghost of Christmas Past.

The Ghost shows Scrooge his childhood, apprenticeship and broken engagement.

Chapter 3

Scrooge is visited by the Ghost of Christmas Present.

The Ghost shows him Christmas at the Cratchits' house and at his nephew's house.

The Ghost shows him Ignorance and Want.

Chapter 4

Scrooge is visited by the Ghost of Christmas Yet To Come.

The Ghost shows him businessmen and poor people talking about a dead man.

The Ghost shows him the Cratchits' home. Tiny Tim has died.

The Ghost shows Scrooge his gravestone. Scrooge vows to change his ways.

Chapter 5

Scrooge buys the Cratchit family a turkey.

Scrooge makes a large donation to a man collecting for charity.

Scrooge spends Christmas at his nephew's house.

Scrooge is generous and kind-hearted from that day on.

a Which of the key events above show **how much** Scrooge changes from the beginning to the end of the novel? Circle Ⓐ them.

b Which of the key events above show **why** Scrooge decides to change? Underline Ⓐ them.

> Compare the key events of Chapter 1 and Chapter 5.

c Look at the key events that you have not circled or underlined. Why do you think Dickens has included these key events in the novel? Write 🖉 **one** or **two** sentences explaining your ideas.

....

....

....

How do I know which are the most significant events in the novel?

Understanding what each key event in the novel contributes to the plot will help you to get the plot straight and identify significant parts of the novel to write about in your responses.

Look at some of the key events in the plot of *A Christmas Carol*.

Chapter 1
- Scrooge is mean to his employee, Bob Cratchit.
- Scrooge is mean to his nephew, Fred.
- Scrooge is mean to a man collecting for charity.
- Scrooge is visited by the Ghost of Jacob Marley.

Chapter 2
- Scrooge is visited by the Ghost of Christmas Past.
- The Ghost shows Scrooge his childhood, apprenticeship and broken engagement.

Chapter 3
- Scrooge is visited by the Ghost of Christmas Present.
- The Ghost shows him Christmas at the Cratchits' house and at his nephew's house.
- The Ghost shows him Ignorance and Want.

Chapter 4
- Scrooge is visited by the Ghost of Christmas Yet To Come.
- The Ghost shows him businessmen and poor people talking about a dead man.
- The Ghost shows him the Cratchits' home. Tiny Tim has died.
- The Ghost shows Scrooge his gravestone. Scrooge vows to change his ways.

Chapter 5
- Scrooge buys the Cratchit family a turkey.
- Scrooge makes a large donation to a man collecting for charity.
- Scrooge spends Christmas at his nephew's house.
- Scrooge is generous and kind-hearted from that day on.

(1) Now think carefully about each of the key events listed above. For each one, ask yourself:

? How would the plot be altered if it were removed?   ? How significant is it to the story?

a Beside each key event, note down ✎ a mark out of 10: give it 1 out of 10 if it is not at all significant, 5 out of 10 if it is quite significant, and 10 out of 10 if it is very significant.

b Tick ✓ the **three** events that you have given the highest mark. Annotate ✎ each one, noting why you have decided it is so significant.

Getting the plot straight

To plan and write an effective response about *A Christmas Carol*, you need to:

- know the key events in each chapter of the novel and the order in which they happen
- understand what each event in the plot contributes to the story
- be able to identify the most significant events in the novel and explain their significance.

Look again at the **first** part of the exam-style question you saw at the start of the unit.

Exam-style question

Starting with this extract, how does Dickens present Scrooge as stubborn and heartless?

Write about:

- how Dickens presents Scrooge as stubborn and heartless in this extract.

① Now look at one student's planning notes, written in response to this exam-style question.

Before this extract: We meet Scrooge for the first time. He is described as 'cold' and 'tight-fisted'.

After this extract: Scrooge refuses to give money to charity.

So in Chapter 1, Scrooge shown as stubborn and heartless to everyone – interested in no one but himself and nothing but his money.

In the extract:
- Contrast of Fred 'a cheerful voice' and Scrooge 'Bah!' emphasises difference/heartlessness.

- Stubborn: lots of exclamations ('Humbug!') and questions ('what right have you to be merry?'), suggesting he is ignoring or questioning everything Fred says.

- Stubbornly refuses to be persuaded by Fred to have a 'Merry Christmas!' and heartlessly tells him that 'every idiot' who says it should be 'boiled' and 'buried' – shocking, violent images.

Shows awareness of **where** in the novel the extract is taken from.

Makes a clear, direct **response** to the question.

Uses **key words** from the question.

Makes a **range of points**.

Supports points with **evidence**.

Comments on the significance of the writer's choices.

For more on analysing the extract, see Units 2 and 3.

Look carefully at the annotations above showing what makes a successful response. Draw lines linking each annotation to a relevant part of the student's plan, to show how the plan will help to make their response to the first part of the question above successful.

Your turn!

After you have read and understood the text, identified its key points and explored the writer's intention, you are ready to tackle **all of the questions** you are likely to be asked in your exam.

You are now going to **write your own answer** in response to the exam-style question.

Exam-style question

Starting with this extract, how does Dickens present Scrooge as stubborn and heartless?

Write about:

• how Dickens presents Scrooge as stubborn and heartless in this extract

• how Dickens presents Scrooge as stubborn and heartless in the novel as a whole.

(1) Look again at some of the key events in the novel.

		✓	✗
Chapter 1	Scrooge is mean to his employee, Bob Cratchit.	☐	☐
	Scrooge is mean to his nephew, Fred.	☐	☐
	Scrooge is mean to a man collecting for charity.	☐	☐
	Scrooge is visited by the Ghost of Jacob Marley.	☐	☐
Chapter 2	Scrooge is visited by the Ghost of Christmas Past.	☐	☐
	The Ghost shows Scrooge his childhood, apprenticeship and broken engagement.	☐	☐
Chapter 3	Scrooge is visited by the Ghost of Christmas Present.	☐	☐
	The Ghost shows him Christmas at the Cratchits' house and at his nephew's house.	☐	☐
	The Ghost shows him Ignorance and Want.	☐	☐
Chapter 4	Scrooge is visited by the Ghost of Christmas Yet To Come.	☐	☐
	The Ghost shows him businessmen and poor people talking about a dead man.	☐	☐
	The Ghost shows him the Cratchits' home. Tiny Tim has died.	☐	☐
	The Ghost shows Scrooge his gravestone. Scrooge vows to change his ways.	☐	☐
Chapter 5	Scrooge buys the Cratchit family a turkey.	☐	☐
	Scrooge makes a large donation to a man collecting for charity.	☐	☐
	Scrooge spends Christmas at his nephew's house.	☐	☐
	Scrooge is generous and kind-hearted from that day on.	☐	☐

a Which key events show Scrooge as stubborn and heartless? Tick ✓ them.

b Think about the other side of the argument: which key events show Scrooge, not as stubborn and heartless, but as kind, generous and willing to change? Cross ✗ them.

c Circle Ⓐ the key events you would choose to write about in your response.

Review your skills

Check up

Review your plan for the exam-style question on page 7. Tick ✓ the column to show how well you think you have done each of the following.

	Not quite ✓	Nearly there ✓	Got it! ✓
identified key events in the novel that show Scrooge as stubborn and heartless	☐	☐	☐
identified key events in the novel that show Scrooge as kind, generous and willing to change	☐	☐	☐
identified key events in the novel that encourage Scrooge to stop being so stubborn and heartless	☐	☐	☐

Look over all of your work in this unit. Note down ✐ the **three** most important things to remember when planning your response to a question about A Christmas Carol.

1. ....
2. ....
3. ....

Need more practice?

Here is another exam-style question, this time relating to the extract from Chapter 1 on page 73 (Extract A).

Exam-style question

Starting with this extract, how does Dickens present the supernatural in A Christmas Carol?

Write about:

• how Dickens presents the supernatural in this extract
• how Dickens presents the supernatural in the novel as a whole. **(30 marks)**

Which key events in the novel would you choose to write ✐ about in your response to this question? You'll find some suggested ideas in the Answers section.

How confident do you feel about each of these **skills?** Colour ✐ in the bars.

1 How do I make sure I know the plot?

2 How can I explore the development of the plot?

3 How do I know which are the most significant events in the novel?

② Analysing the extract

This unit will help you to explore the extract in the exam question about *A Christmas Carol*. The skills you will build are to:

• select relevant points to make in your analysis

• develop your analysis

• structure your analysis.

In the exam you will face questions like the one below. This is about the extract on the next page. At the end of the unit you will **write one paragraph** in response to this question, **focusing on the extract**.

Exam-style question

Starting with this extract, how does Dickens present Scrooge as self-contained and solitary?

Write about:

• how Dickens presents Scrooge in this extract

• how Dickens presents Scrooge as self-contained and solitary in the novel as a whole.

(30 marks)

Before you tackle the question you will work through three key questions in the **skills boosts** to help you analyse the extract.

| ① How do I choose the points I need to make? | ② How do I develop my analysis? | ③ How do I structure a paragraph of analysis? |

Read the extract on the next page from Chapter 1 of *A Christmas Carol*.

As you read, think about the following:

| What has happened before this extract? What happens after this extract? | How does Dickens present Bob Cratchit in this extract? | How does this compare with Dickens' presentation of Scrooge in this extract? |

Exam-style question

Read the following extract from Chapter 1 of *A Christmas Carol*.

In this extract it is Christmas Eve. Bob Cratchit and Scrooge have finished work for the day.

Extract A | Chapter 1 of *A Christmas Carol* by Charles Dickens

The office was closed in a twinkling, and the clerk, with the long ends of his white comforter dangling below his waist (for he boasted no great-coat), went down a slide on **Cornhill**, at the end of a lane of boys, twenty times, in honour of its being Christmas Eve, and then ran home to Camden Town as hard as he could pelt, to play at blindman's-buff.

5 Scrooge took his melancholy dinner in his usual melancholy tavern; and having read all the newspapers, and beguiled the rest of the evening with his banker's-book, went home to bed. He lived in chambers which had once belonged to his deceased partner. They were a gloomy suite of rooms, in a lowering pile of building up a yard, where it had so little business to be, that one could scarcely help fancying it must have run there when it was a young house, playing at hide-and-seek with other houses, and have forgotten the way out again. It was old enough
10 now, and dreary enough, for nobody lived in it but Scrooge, the other rooms being all let out as offices. The yard was so dark that even Scrooge, who knew its every stone, was fain to grope with his hands. The fog and frost so hung about the black old gateway of the house, that it seemed as if the Genius of the Weather sat in mournful meditation on the threshold.

Now, it is a fact, that there was nothing at all particular about the knocker on the door, except that it was very large.
15 It is also a fact, that Scrooge had seen it night and morning during his whole residence in that place; also that Scrooge had as little of what is called fancy about him as any man in the City of London, even including – which is a bold word – the corporation, aldermen, and livery. Let it also be borne in mind that Scrooge had not bestowed one thought on Marley, since his last mention of his seven-years' dead partner that afternoon. And then let any man explain to me, if he can, how it happened that Scrooge, having his key in the lock of the door, saw in the knocker,
20 without its undergoing any intermediate process of change: not a knocker, but Marley's face.

Marley's face. It was not in impenetrable shadow as the other objects in the yard were, but had a dismal light about it, like a bad lobster in a dark cellar. It was not angry or ferocious, but looked at Scrooge as Marley used to look: with ghostly spectacles turned up upon its ghostly forehead. The hair was curiously stirred, as if by breath or hot-air; and, though the eyes were wide open, they were perfectly motionless. That, and its livid colour, made it horrible;
25 but its horror seemed to be in spite of the face and beyond its control, rather than a part of its own expression.

As Scrooge looked fixedly at this phenomenon, it was a knocker again.

To say that he was not startled, or that his blood was not conscious of a terrible sensation to which it had been a stranger from infancy, would be untrue. But he put his hand upon the key he had relinquished, turned it sturdily, walked in, and lighted his candle.

Cornhill a street in London

How do I choose the points I need to make?

The first thing you need to do is to identify which parts of the extract you can explore further in your response to the question.

Look again at the exam-style question you are exploring.

Exam-style question

Starting with this extract, how does Dickens present Scrooge as self-contained and solitary?

(1) Now look through the extract on page 10, focusing on each section in turn.

1. Cratchit goes down a slide twenty times, then runs home for a game of blindman's-buff. [lines 2–4] ☐

2. Scrooge eats alone, looks at his banker's book and goes home. [lines 5–6] ☐

3. Scrooge's chambers are described. [lines 7–13] ☐

4. The door knocker turns into the face of Jacob Marley. [lines 19–20] ☐

5. The door knocker, in the shape of Marley's face, is described. [lines 21–25] ☐

6. The door knocker is a door knocker again. Scrooge is startled. [lines 26–28] ☐

a Decide which **three** sections reveal the most about how Dickens presents Scrooge as self-contained and solitary. Label 🖉 them A, B and C.

Think about:
- Bob Cratchit's journey home compared with Scrooge's journey home
- what the description of Scrooge's chambers reveals about him.

b Note 🖉 below what each of the sections you have chosen reveals about how Dickens presents Scrooge as self-contained and solitary.

A

B

C

② How do I develop my analysis?

To develop your analysis, you need to think about how the characters, events or setting are described in the extract, and what this reveals about the aspect of the novel that you are exploring. Your ideas need to be supported by evidence from the extract.

Look again at the exam-style question you are exploring.

Exam-style question

Starting with this extract, how does Dickens present Scrooge as self-contained and solitary?

① Now look at one speech from the extract that reveals something about power and the desire for power.

> He lived in chambers which had once belonged to his deceased partner. They were a gloomy suite of rooms, in a lowering pile of building up a yard, where it had so little business to be, that one could scarcely help fancying it must have run there when it was a young house, playing at hide-and-seek with other houses, and have forgotten the way out again. It was old enough now, and dreary enough, for nobody lived in it but Scrooge, the other rooms being all let out as offices. The yard was so dark that even Scrooge, who knew its every stone, was fain to grope with his hands. The fog and frost so hung about the black old gateway of the house, that it seemed as if the Genius of the Weather sat in mournful meditation on the threshold.

a What impression does this description give you of Scrooge's home? Sum it up ✐ in a **few** words.

Underline all the words or phrases used to describe his home. Focus on those.

....

b Why might Dickens have chosen to give Scrooge a home like this one? Write ✐ **one** or **two** sentences explaining your ideas.

....

....

....

....

c Look again at your answers above. How does this description of Scrooge's home help to show him as self-contained and solitary? ✐

....

....

....

....

d Which parts of the description show this most clearly? Choose **two** short quotations and underline Ⓐ them.

② Now choose another section of the extract that shows Scrooge as self-contained and solitary.

a Annotate ✐ the text on page 10, noting down:
- the impression that the section creates
- how it helps to show Scrooge as self-contained and solitary.

b Then underline Ⓐ **two** short quotations to support your ideas.

How do I structure a paragraph of analysis?

Each paragraph of your analysis should include:
- a key point focusing on the key words in the question
- evidence from the text to support your point
- comments on the evidence and its impact
- a summary of your response to the question.

You can structure these four elements in different ways.

> You can build your skill in analysing the extract in more depth and detail in Unit 3.

Look at the sentences from one paragraph of a student's response to this exam-style question.

Exam-style question

Starting with this extract, how does Dickens present Scrooge as self-contained and solitary?

1 Tick ✓ the sentences you would include in a paragraph in response to the exam-style question.

		✓	✎
A	The description of Scrooge's home powerfully develops the reader's impression that he lives a self-contained and solitary life.	☐	☐
B	His home is 'a gloomy suite of rooms' which are 'up a yard'.	☐	☐
C	Dickens describes how 'the fog and frost ... hung about the black old gateway'.	☐	☐
D	Dickens presents Scrooge's home to reflect his character because, like him, it is cold, unwelcoming and set apart from the rest of society.	☐	☐
E	The gateway, which should be a welcoming entrance to his home, is frozen and forbidding.	☐	☐
F	The building is set apart and isolated from all the other nearby houses, reflecting Scrooge's gloomy, solitary nature.	☐	☐

2 How would you sequence your chosen sentences in a paragraph? Number ✎ them.

3 Write ✎ a paragraph on paper using your chosen sentences and linking them with some or all of the following phrases.

Similarly	In this way	This suggests that	For example,	It implies that

4 Look at the sentences you have chosen and sequenced.
   a Which sentences make a key point? Label ✎ them '**Key point**'.
   b Which support a key point using evidence? Label ✎ them '**Evidence**'.
   c Which comment on the evidence and its impact? Label ✎ them '**Comment**'.
   d Which show the writer's response to the question? Label ✎ them '**Response**'.

Analysing the extract

To analyse the extract effectively, you need to:

- identify the parts of the extract that are relevant to the question
- explore what these parts suggest about the focus of the question
- structure your paragraphs of analysis to include a key point supported by evidence, a comment on its impact and a response to the question.

Look at the exam-style question you saw at the start of the unit.

Exam-style question

Starting with this extract, how does Dickens present Scrooge as self-contained and solitary?

(1) Look at this paragraph, taken from a student's response to this question. It focuses on the extract on page 10, Extract A.

> In this extract, Scrooge is clearly shown to lead a self-contained and solitary life. The reader is told that, after leaving his office, he eats his 'melancholy dinner in his usual melancholy tavern', which suggests that everything he does and everywhere he goes is 'melancholy'. He spends 'the rest of the evening with his banker's-book', which implies that, instead of spending the evening in a tavern with a friend or with family, he would rather spend it with his money. The impression created in this sentence is of an isolated, solitary man who is interested only in business and profit.

a Which of the following has this student achieved? Tick (✓) them.

A Identified a part of the extract that is relevant to the question.

B Made a key point.

C Supported it with evidence.

D Commented on its impact.

E Responded to the question.

b Highlight (✐) and label (✐) where in the paragraph this student has achieved B, C, D and E.

Your turn!

You are now going to **write one or two paragraphs** in response to the exam-style question below, **focusing on these sections** of Extract A on page 10.

1

The office was closed in a twinkling, and the clerk, with the long ends of his white comforter dangling below his waist (for he boasted no great-coat), went down a slide on Cornhill, at the end of a lane of boys, twenty times, in honour of its being Christmas Eve, and then ran home to Camden Town as hard as he could pelt, to play at blindman's-buff.

2

Scrooge took his melancholy dinner in his usual melancholy tavern; and having read all the newspapers, and beguiled the rest of the evening with his banker's-book, went home to bed.

Exam-style question

Starting with this extract, how does Dickens present Scrooge as self-contained and solitary?

Write about:

• how Dickens presents Scrooge in this extract

• how Dickens presents Scrooge as self-contained and solitary in the novel as a whole.

(30 marks)

(1) Look at the first section from the extract above. What does this suggest about Bob Cratchit? ✎

First section

(2) Look at the second section from the extract above. What does this suggest about Scrooge? ✎

Second section

(3) Think about both sections. How is Dickens contrasting Bob Cratchit and Scrooge here? ✎

You may want to use some of the ideas below, or use your own.

| child-like | joy | family |
| money | miserable | alone |

How is Scrooge presented, compared with Bob Cratchit?

(4) Underline Ⓐ short, relevant quotations in the sections above that you can use in your response.

(5) On paper, write ✎ **one** or **two** paragraphs in response to the exam-style question above.

Review your skills

Check up

Review your response to the exam-style question on page 15. Tick ✓ the column to show how well you think you have done each of the following.

	Not quite ✓	Nearly there ✓	Got it! ✓
made a relevant key point	☐	☐	☐
supported my key point with relevant evidence	☐	☐	☐
commented on the impact of my evidence	☐	☐	☐
responded to the question	☐	☐	☐

Need more practice?

Here is another exam-style question, this time relating to the extract from Chapter 1 on page 73 (Extract A).

Exam-style question

Starting with this extract, how does Dickens present the supernatural in *A Christmas Carol*?

Write about:

- how Dickens presents the supernatural in this extract
- how Dickens presents the supernatural in the novel as a whole.

(30 marks)

Write 🖉 **one** or **two** paragraphs in response to this question, focusing on the extract only.

You'll find some suggested ideas in the Answers section.

How confident do you feel about each of these **skills?** Colour 🖉 in the bars.

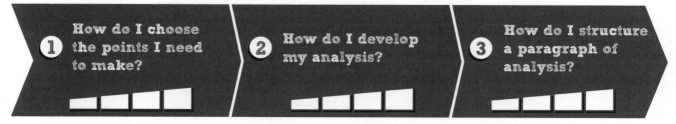

1 How do I choose the points I need to make?

2 How do I develop my analysis?

3 How do I structure a paragraph of analysis?

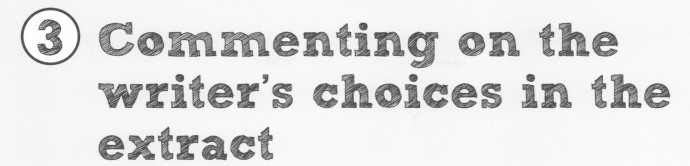

③ Commenting on the writer's choices in the extract

This unit will help you to comment on Dickens' choices in the extract from *A Christmas Carol*. The skills you will build are to:

- identify relevant language choices to comment on
- identify relevant choices of sentence form and structure to comment on
- make effective comments on the writer's choices.

In the exam you will face questions like the one below. This is about the extract on the next page. At the end of the unit you will **write one or two paragraphs** in response to this question, **focusing on the extract**.

Exam-style question

Starting with this extract, how does Dickens present the change in Scrooge's nature?

Write about:

- how Dickens presents the change in Scrooge in this extract
- how Dickens presents the change in Scrooge in the novel as a whole.

(30 marks)

Before you tackle the question you will work through three key questions in the **skills boosts** to help you comment on the writer's choices in the extract.

① How do I identify significant language choices?

② How do I identify significant sentence forms and structural choices?

③ How do I comment on the writer's choices?

Read the extract on the next page from Chapter 2 of *A Christmas Carol*.

As you read, think about the following:

How does Dickens present Scrooge *before* this extract?

How does Dickens present Scrooge in this extract?

How does Dickens present the change in Scrooge's nature *after* this extract?

Exam-style question

Read the following extract from Chapter 2 of *A Christmas Carol*.

In this extract the Ghost of Christmas Past shows Scrooge some scenes from his childhood.

Extract A | Chapter 2 of *A Christmas Carol* by Charles Dickens

The city had entirely vanished. Not a vestige of it was to be seen. The darkness and the mist had vanished with it, for it was a clear, cold, winter day, with snow upon the ground.

"Good Heaven!" said Scrooge, clasping his hands together, as he looked about him. "I was bred in this place. I was a boy here!"

5 The Spirit gazed upon him mildly. Its gentle touch, though it had been light and instantaneous, appeared still present to the old man's sense of feeling. He was conscious of a thousand odours floating in the air, each one connected with a thousand thoughts, and hopes, and joys, and cares long, long, forgotten.

"Your lip is trembling," said the Ghost. "And what is that upon your cheek?"

Scrooge muttered, with an unusual catching in his voice, that it was a pimple; and begged the Ghost to lead him
10 where he would.

"You recollect the way?" inquired the Spirit.

"Remember it!" cried Scrooge with fervour – "I could walk it blindfold."

"Strange to have forgotten it for so many years!" observed the Ghost. "Let us go on."

They walked along the road; Scrooge recognising every gate, and post, and tree; until a little market-town appeared
15 in the distance, with its bridge, its church, and winding river. Some shaggy ponies now were seen trotting towards them with boys upon their backs, who called to other boys in country gigs and carts, driven by farmers. All these boys were in great spirits, and shouted to each other, until the broad fields were so full of merry music, that the crisp air laughed to hear it.

"These are but shadows of the things that have been," said the Ghost. "They have no consciousness of us."

20 The jocund travellers came on; and as they came, Scrooge knew and named them every one. Why was he rejoiced beyond all bounds to see them! Why did his cold eye glisten, and his heart leap up as they went past! Why was he filled with gladness when he heard them give each other Merry Christmas, as they parted at cross-roads and bye-ways, for their several homes! What was merry Christmas to Scrooge? Out upon merry Christmas! What good had it ever done to him?

25 "The school is not quite deserted," said the Ghost. "A solitary child, neglected by his friends, is left there still."

Scrooge said he knew it. And he sobbed.

How do I identify significant language choices?

Identifying significant language choices that Dickens has made in an extract can reveal a great deal about the characters and their thoughts and feelings.

1 Look at this paragraph from Extract A on page 18. It describes Scrooge's reaction when he recognises the place to which the Ghost of Christmas Past has brought him.

| "Good Heaven!" said Scrooge, | clasping his hands together, | as he looked about him. | "I was bred in this place. | I was a boy here." |

a Focus on each **section** of text. Which sections show Scrooge's reaction most strongly? Underline (A) **two** choices.

b Now look at each **word or phrase** in the sections you have underlined. Which words or phrases show Scrooge's reaction most strongly? Circle (A) **two** choices.

c What does Dickens' choice of these words or phrases suggest about Scrooge's thoughts and feelings? Write (✏) **one** or **two** sentences summing up your ideas.

....

....

....

2 Now look at two more sections of text from Extract A.

a Annotate (✏) each section, noting what you learn from each one about Scrooge's thoughts and feelings.

b Which **one** or **two** words or phrases in each section most strongly show these thoughts and feelings? Circle (A) them.

c What does each word or phrase you have circled suggest about Scrooge? Annotate (✏) the words and phrases you have circled.

A

"Your lip is trembling," said the Ghost. "And what is that upon your cheek?"

Scrooge muttered, with an unusual catching in his voice, that it was a pimple; and begged the Ghost to lead him where he would.

B

"The school is not quite deserted," said the Ghost. "A solitary child, neglected by his friends, is left there still."

Scrooge said he knew it. And he sobbed.

3 How do the two sections of text above suggest that Scrooge is beginning to change? Write (✏) **one** or **two** sentences explaining your ideas.

....

....

② How do I identify significant sentence forms and structural choices?

Writers structure their sentences to add impact to the ideas they want to convey to the reader.

① Look at this section from the extract on page 18.

> The jocund travellers came on; and as they came, Scrooge knew and named them every one. Why was he rejoiced beyond all bounds to see them! Why did his cold eye glisten, and his heart leap up as they went past! Why was he filled with gladness when he heard them give each other Merry Christmas, as they parted at cross-roads and bye-ways, for their several homes! What was merry Christmas to Scrooge? Out upon merry Christmas! What good had it ever done to him?
>
> "The school is not quite deserted," said the Ghost. "A solitary child, neglected by his friends, is left there still."
>
> Scrooge said he knew it. And he sobbed.

Underline Ⓐ any of the sentence scraps below that when combined would accurately describe what this section suggests about Scrooge.

You could use different colours to show different valid combinations.

In this section of the extract, Dickens | shows | suggests

Scrooge's | the Ghost's

confusion | anguish | determination | shock

② Look again at the extract.

ⓐ Identify and label 🖉 **two** sentences that use sentence forms **A, B, C** or **D** in the extract.

A Dickens uses a long sentence

B Dickens uses a short sentence

C Dickens uses a rhetorical question

D Dickens uses an exclamation

ⓑ Now choose **one** of the sentence forms you have identified in the extract above. What does your chosen sentence suggest about the character of Scrooge? Write 🖉 **one** sentence explaining your ideas. Use some of the sentence scraps in question ① above to help you.

In sentence ...., Dickens suggests that ....

....

....

ⓒ How does Dickens' choice of sentence form add to the impact of this idea? Write 🖉 a **second** sentence on paper explaining your views, using some of the sentence scraps below to help you.

Dickens uses a .... to | emphasise | highlight

that Scrooge will not admit what he is feeling.

that Scrooge is beginning to change.

that Scrooge will not change.

the variety of mixed emotions Scrooge is experiencing.

3 How do I comment on the writer's choices?

An effective comment on the writer's choices highlights the **choice** the writer has made, and comments on its **effect**.

Look at some of the different kinds of comment on **language** and **structure** you could make on this sentence from Extract A on page 18.

> He was conscious of a thousand odours floating in the air, each one connected with a thousand thoughts, and hopes, and joys, and cares long, long, forgotten.

Language

You can comment on...	choice	+	effect	
• a specific type of word	*The number 'a thousand'*		*highlights their impact on Scrooge*	☐
• the connotations or implications of a specific word or phrase	*The phrase 'hopes, and joys'*		*suggests Scrooge's happiness as a child*	☐
• the kind of language in the whole sentence.	*The contrast of the 'hopes, and joys' with 'cares'*		*emphasises the different emotions Scrooge is experiencing*	☐

Structure

You can comment on...	choice	+	effect	
• the length of the sentence	*long sentence using a list*		*shows how many 'thoughts, hopes, joys and cares' he has forgotten.*	☐
• repetition	*The repetition of 'long'*		*emphasises how much Scrooge has changed since his childhood.*	☐
• the order of the words or ideas in the sentence.	*The final phrase 'long, long, forgotten'*		*gives it even greater emphasis.*	☐

(1) Which of these would you include in your comments? Tick ✓ them.

(2) Now think about another quotation from the extract.

> "The school is not quite deserted," said the Ghost. "A solitary child, neglected by his friends, is left there still."
>
> Scrooge said he knew it. And he sobbed.

Think about: how the Ghost describes the child in the school and how this changes your impressions of Scrooge – and how Dickens describes Scrooge's reaction.

Write ✏ **one** or **two** sentences on paper, commenting on Dickens' choices of language, sentence form and structure in this section.

Commenting on the writer's choices in the extract

To comment effectively on Dickens' choices in the extract, you need to:

- identify relevant evidence from the extract to support your ideas
- select significant language and/or sentence forms and/or structural choices in the evidence you have identified
- highlight in your evidence the choices that Dickens has made and comment on their effect.

(For more help on structuring a paragraph of analysis, see Unit 2.)

Look at this exam-style question you saw at the start of the unit on page 17.

Exam-style question

Starting with this extract, how does Dickens present the change in Scrooge's nature?

(1) Can you identify all the different things the student has included in this paragraph?
Link 🖉 the annotations to the paragraph to show where the student has included them.

Key features of an effective paragraph of analysis:

key point focusing on the key words in the question

evidence from the text to support the point

comments on the evidence and its impact

a response to the question

When Scrooge recognises the place that the Ghost has brought him to see, Dickens clearly shows it has a significant effect on him: "'Good Heaven!' said Scrooge, clasping his hands together'. The short exclamation at the beginning of this sentence emphasises his surprise, while the verb 'clasping' could suggest powerful feelings of happiness or anxiety. Scrooge then goes on to explain "'I was bred in this place. I was a boy here.'" Dickens uses short sentences here to suggest how quickly Scrooge is speaking, suggesting his surprise and excitement at seeing it again. Scrooge's reaction at the start of the extract shows the impact these scenes from his childhood are having on him, encouraging the reader to think that his uncharacteristically enthusiastic and positive reaction may show he is starting to change.

Key features of an effective comment on the writer's choices:

a comment on language choice(s)

a comment on choice(s) of structure or sentence form

Your turn!

You are now going to **write one or two paragraphs** in response to the exam-style question below, **focusing on Extract A on page 18.**

focusing on Extract A on page 18.

Exam-style question

Starting with this extract, how does Dickens present the change in Scrooge's nature?

Write about:

- how Dickens presents the change in Scrooge in this extract
- how Dickens presents the change in Scrooge in the novel as a whole.

(30 marks)

(1) Choose **one short section** of the extract that clearly suggests that Scrooge is beginning to change. Circle (A) it on page 18.

(2) Now look closely at the section you have chosen. Select **one** short quotation that clearly shows **how** Scrooge is beginning to change. Underline (A) it on page 18.

(3) Think about words or phrases in your chosen quotation that make a significant contribution to your impressions of Scrooge and the ways in which he is changing.

   (a) Which words or phrases reveal something significant about Scrooge's thoughts or feelings at this point in the story? Highlight (✏) them on page 18.

   (b) What do those words and phrases suggest about Scrooge's thoughts or feelings? Annotate (✏) them.

   (c) How do these thoughts or feelings show Scrooge is beginning to change? Add (✏) to your annotations.

(4) Now think about Dickens' choices of structure or sentence form in your chosen quotation. Think about:

- the length of the sentence(s)
- the order of the words or ideas in the sentence(s)
- any repetition.

Do Dickens' choices of structure or sentence form in your chosen quotation make a significant contribution to your impressions of Scrooge and the ways in which he is changing? How? Annotate (✏) your chosen quotation with your ideas.

(5) Using all the ideas you have noted, write (✏) **one** paragraph on paper in response to the exam-style question above.

(6) Repeat questions (1)–(5), focusing on a different section of the extract. (✏)

Review your skills

Check up

Review your response to the exam-style question on page 23. Tick ✓ the column to show how well you think you have done each of the following.

	Not quite ✓	Nearly there ✓	Got it! ✓
structured an effective paragraph of analysis in response to the question	☐	☐	☐
commented on Dickens' language choices	☐	☐	☐
commented on Dickens' choices of structure and/or sentence form	☐	☐	☐

Need more practice?

Here is another exam-style question, this time relating to the extract from Chapter 2 on page 74 (Extract B).

Exam-style question

Starting with this extract, explore how Dickens presents money in *A Christmas Carol*.

Write about:

• how Dickens presents money in this extract
• how Dickens presents money in the novel as a whole.

(30 marks)

Write 🖊 **one** or **two** paragraphs on paper in response to this question, **focusing on the extract only**.

You'll find some suggested ideas in the Answers section.

How confident do you feel about each of these **skills?** Colour 🖊 in the bars.

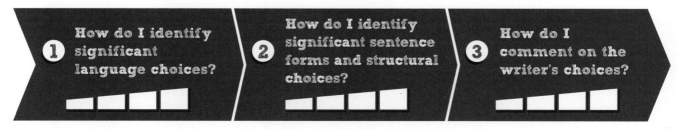

1 How do I identify significant language choices?

2 How do I identify significant sentence forms and structural choices?

3 How do I comment on the writer's choices?

④ Exploring themes and characters

This unit will help you to explore how the characters and themes of *A Christmas Carol* develop in the novel, and help you to develop your response to them. The skills you will build are to:

• track how characters develop in the novel
• explore themes in the novel
• comment on the development of characters and themes in the novel.

In the exam you will face questions like the one below. This is about the extract on the next page. At the end of the unit you will **plan and write one or two paragraphs** in response to this question.

Exam-style question

Starting with this extract, how does Dickens present the festival of Christmas in *A Christmas Carol?*

Write about:

• how Dickens presents Christmas in this extract
• how Dickens presents Christmas in the novel as a whole.

(30 marks)

Before you tackle the question you will work through three key questions in the **skills boosts** to help you explore the novel's themes and characters.

 1 How do I track the development of a character?   **2 How do I explore a theme?**   **3 How do I comment on the development of character or theme?**

Read the extract on the next page from Chapter 2 of *A Christmas Carol.*

As you read, think about the following:

What has happened before this extract? What happens after this extract? ☐	How does Dickens present the celebration of Christmas in this extract? ☐	What impact does the scene described have on Scrooge? ☐

Exam-style question

Read the following extract from Chapter 2 of *A Christmas Carol*.

In this extract the Ghost of Christmas Past shows Scrooge a scene from his past: the celebration of Christmas at Mr Fezziwig's.

Extract A | Chapter 2 of *A Christmas Carol* by Charles Dickens

When the clock struck eleven, this domestic ball broke up. Mr. and Mrs. Fezziwig took their stations, one on either side of the door, and shaking hands with every person individually as he or she went out, wished him or her a Merry Christmas. When everybody had retired but the two 'prentices, they did the same to them; and thus the cheerful voices died away, and the lads were left to their beds; which were under a counter in the back-shop.

5 During the whole of this time, Scrooge had acted like a man out of his wits. His heart and soul were in the scene, and with his former self. He corroborated everything, remembered everything, enjoyed everything, and underwent the strangest agitation. It was not until now, when the bright faces of his former self and Dick were turned from them, that he remembered the Ghost, and became conscious that it was looking full upon him, while the light upon its head burnt very clear.

10 "A small matter," said the Ghost, "to make these silly folks so full of gratitude."

"Small!" echoed Scrooge.

The Spirit signed to him to listen to the two apprentices, who were pouring out their hearts in praise of Fezziwig: and when he had done so, said, "Why! Is it not? He has spent but a few pounds of your mortal money: three or four, perhaps. Is that so much that he deserves this praise?"

15 "It isn't that," said Scrooge, heated by the remark, and speaking unconsciously like his former, not his latter, self. "It isn't that, Spirit. He has the power to render us happy or unhappy; to make our service light or burdensome; a pleasure or a toil. Say that his power lies in words and looks; in things so slight and insignificant that it is impossible to add and count 'em up: what then? The happiness he gives, is quite as great as if it cost a fortune."

He felt the Spirit's glance, and stopped.

20 "What is the matter?" asked the Ghost.

"Nothing particular," said Scrooge.

"Something, I think?" the Ghost insisted.

"No," said Scrooge, "No. I should like to be able to say a word or two to my clerk just now! That's all."

How do I track the development of a character?

Scrooge is the key character in *A Christmas Carol*. To write effectively about him in the novel as a whole, you need to think about Dickens' presentation of **how** he develops and **why**.

① Think about how Scrooge is presented in **Chapter 1, at the beginning** of the novel.

- he hates Christmas and refuses to spend it with his nephew, Fred
- he refuses to give to charity
- he grudgingly allows Bob Cratchit one day off at Christmas

How would you sum up the character of Scrooge at the start of the novel? Tick ✓ any of the words below and/or add 🖉 your own ideas.

mean	cruel	heartless	isolated	selfish	bitter	fearful		
☐	☐	☐	☐	☐	☐	☐		

② Now think about how Scrooge is presented in **Chapter 5, at the end** of the novel.

- he spends Christmas with his nephew, Fred

- he buys the Cratchits a turkey, increases Bob's salary and promises to help his family

- he makes a large donation to charity

How would you sum up the character of Scrooge at the end of the novel? Note 🖉 up to **five** words.

> Look at the words you chose to describe him in question ①. What has changed?

③ Now look at some of the key events in the novel showing the development of Scrooge's character. In **Chapter 2**, the Ghost of Christmas Past shows Scrooge…

… Christmas at Fezziwig's.

"I should like to be able to say a word or two to my clerk just now!"

/10

… himself as a lonely, neglected child.

"There was a boy singing a Christmas Carol at my door last night. I should like to have given him something"

/10

In **Chapter 3**, the Ghost of Christmas Present shows Scrooge…

… the Cratchits at Christmas. The Ghost says that he sees Tiny Tim's seat vacant in the near future.

"Oh no, kind Spirit! say he will be spared."

/10

… Christmas at his nephew's.

… he begged like a boy to be allowed to stay until the guests departed.

/10

In **Chapter 4**, the Ghost of Christmas Yet To Come shows Scrooge…

… a wealthy dead man's belongings stolen by a group of poor people.

"The case of this unhappy man might be my own."

/10

… his own grave. He realises that he is the wealthy dead man.

"I will honour Christmas in my heart, and try to keep it all the year."

/10

How significant is each of these scenes in showing the change in Scrooge's character in the novel? Give 🖉 each one a mark out of ten: 1/10 = not at all significant; 10/10 = highly significant.

② How do I explore a theme?

To explore how Dickens presents a theme in the novel, you need to identify key events in which that theme is featured.

① Look at some of the **key themes** in *A Christmas Carol* below. Complete (✏️) these notes with **a key event** in which each theme is relevant.

transformation	
money	
poverty	*Scrooge is shown Ignorance and Want by the Ghost of Christmas Present.*
family	
Christmas	
justice	*Marley's ghost is bound in the chain he 'forged in life'.*

② A **key theme** is an idea that Dickens explores in different ways at different points in the novel. Look at some of the key points at which Dickens explores the theme of **poverty**.

- The Cratchit family enjoys a poor but happy Christmas.

- Ignorance and Want represent the problems of poverty in Victorian society.

- Tiny Tim will die in the future because of his family's poverty.

- Scrooge's belongings are stolen by a group of poor people when he dies.

How does Dickens present poverty in the novel? Circle (Ⓐ) any of the ideas below.

positive		neutral	negative	
less important than happiness and family	Only a problem for lazy people, easily solved	an unavoidable fact of life	corrupting	deadly

③ Now think about **the theme of Christmas**.

ⓐ Note (✏️) down on paper **two** or **three** significant key events in the novel that feature the celebration of Christmas.

ⓑ How does Dickens present the theme of Christmas in the novel? Write (✏️) **one** or **two** sentences explaining your ideas.

....

....

....

3 How do I comment on the development of character or theme?

One way to explore how characters and themes develop in a novel is to **compare** how they are presented at different key points in the story.

1 Compare the key points below about Scrooge in the **present**, when he is introduced at the start of the novel, with the key points about his **past**.

Past

A Scrooge is left at school at Christmas: 'A solitary child, neglected by his friends'.	**B** His sister persuades their father to allow Scrooge to come home. She explains: "Father is so much kinder than he used to be."	**C** Scrooge enthusiastically prepares for Fezziwig's Christmas party.	**D** Scrooge is rejected by his fiancée, Belle, because he loves money more than her.

Present

E Scrooge is 'self-contained, and solitary as an oyster'.	**F** Scrooge is interested only in money.	**G** Scrooge hates Christmas.

a Which of these key points show that Scrooge has changed from the past to the present? Draw 🖉 **solid** lines linking them.

b Which of these key points show that Scrooge has **not** changed from the past to the present? Draw 🖉 **dotted** lines linking them.

c What effect might Scrooge's past have had on his present? Write 🖉 **one** or **two** sentences explaining your ideas.

....

....

....

2 Look at these four key moments in the novel where the theme of money is shown.

- In Chapter 2, Fezziwig spends just a few pounds on a Christmas party.

- In Chapter 2, Belle breaks off her engagement to Scrooge because of his love of money.

- In Chapter 3, the Cratchit family enjoy Christmas despite their poverty.

- In Chapter 3, the Ghost says Tiny Tim will die if nothing happens to change his future life.

a Think about how the theme of money is presented in the novel. Tick ✓ any of the statements below that you agree with.

A	*The wealthy should share their money.*	☐	C	*Money can be used to create happiness.*	☐
B	*Lack of money causes unhappiness.*	☐	D	*Money does not make you happy.*	☐

b Write 🖉 **one** or **two** sentences on paper summing up your thoughts about the presentation of money in *A Christmas Carol*.

Exploring themes and characters

To explore the themes and characters in *A Christmas Carol* effectively, you need to:
- identify significant key events in the novel in which those characters or themes are shown
- compare how they are presented in those key events.

Look at this exam-style question you saw at the start of the unit.

Exam-style question

Starting with this extract, how does Dickens present the festival of Christmas in *A Christmas Carol*?

Write about:
- how Dickens presents Christmas in this extract
- how Dickens presents Christmas in the novel as a whole.

(1) Now look at these two paragraphs, written by a student in response to the exam-style question above.

> At the beginning of the novel, Dickens presents Christmas by contrasting Scrooge's "Bah! Humbug!" attitude to Christmas with that of his nephew, Fred, who thinks Christmas is a time for celebration and happiness. Scrooge even refuses to spend Christmas with his nephew. This contrast shows how miserable and hard-hearted Scrooge is because he will not change his ways even for Christmas. It shows he is the exact opposite of Christmas. He is mean, miserable and isolated, whereas Christmas is a time for generosity, happiness and family.
>
> This impression of Christmas is shown in Chapter 3. For example, the Ghost of Christmas Present shows Scrooge a vision of the streets of London in which the poor are happy getting ready for Christmas. The Ghost shows him the Cratchits gathering together to enjoy a feast of goose and a plum pudding at Christmas even though they are poor. The Ghost shows him Christmas at Fred's house where he and his wife and their friends enjoy games and music, showing that happiness at Christmas is not expensive, even for the richer people of society. Dickens presents this very positive image of Christmas throughout the novel, until eventually Scrooge is persuaded to join in with it.

a Circle (A) and label (✏) **all** the key events in the novel that this student has referred to in these paragraphs.

b Underline (A) and label (✏) where in these paragraphs this student **comments** on how Dickens presents Christmas in these key events.

c Highlight (✏) and label (✏) where in these paragraphs this student **compares** key events in which Christmas is presented in the novel as a whole to develop their ideas.

Your turn!

You are now going to **write two paragraphs** in response to the exam-style question.

1 Which key events in the novel could you focus on in your response? Note 🖉 **four** of your ideas below.

Think about:

> ❓ What does each of these events suggest about the theme of Christmas?

> ❓ Is the theme of Christmas always presented in this way? Or are there other key events in the novel which present this theme in a different light?

1

2

3

4

2 Now compare how the theme of Christmas is presented in the different key events you have noted above. What does your comparison suggest about the way in which Christmas is presented in the novel? Add 🖉 to your notes.

3 Write 🖉 your paragraphs on paper in response to the exam-style question above.

Review your skills

Check up

Review your response to the exam-style question on page 31. Tick ✓ the column to show how well you think you have done each of the following.

	Not quite ✓	Nearly there ✓	Got it! ✓
identified key events in the novel showing the theme of Christmas	☐	☐	☐
commented on how Christmas is presented in each key event	☐	☐	☐
developed my ideas by comparing how Christmas is presented in key events	☐	☐	☐

Need more practice?

Here is another exam-style question, this time relating to the extract from Chapter 2 on page 74 (Extract B).

Exam-style question

Starting with this extract, explore how Dickens presents money in *A Christmas Carol*.

Write about:

• how Dickens presents money in this extract

• how Dickens presents money in the novel as a whole.

(30 marks)

Write ✎ **two** paragraphs in response to this question, focusing on the second bullet point: **the novel as a whole.**

You'll find some suggested ideas in the Answers section.

How confident do you feel about each of these **skills**? Colour ✎ in the bars.

1 How do I track the development of a character?

2 How do I explore a theme?

3 How do I comment on the development of character or theme?

⑤ Planning your response

This unit will help you to plan your response to the exam question. The skills you will build are to:

- develop a critical judgement in response to the focus of the exam question
- support your judgement with relevant points
- sequence your points to build a successful argument in support of your judgement.

In the exam you will face a question like the one below. This is about the extract on the next page. At the end of the unit you will **plan and write your own response** to this question.

Exam-style question

Starting with this extract, how does Dickens present families in *A Christmas Carol*?

Write about:
- how Dickens presents families in this extract
- how Dickens presents families in the novel as a whole.

(30 marks)

Before you tackle the question you will work through three key questions in the **skills boosts** to help you plan your response.

① How do I make a critical judgement? → **②** How do I gather relevant points? → **③** How do I sequence my points?

Read the extract on the next page from Chapter 3 of *A Christmas Carol*.

As you read, think about the following:

What has happened before this extract? What happens after this extract?

How does Dickens present the Cratchit family in this extract?

How does the Cratchit family compare with other families presented in the novel?

Read the following extract from Chapter 3 of *A Christmas Carol*.

In this extract, the Ghost of Christmas Present is showing Scrooge a vision of Christmas at the Cratchit family's house.

Extract A | Chapter 3 of *A Christmas Carol* by Charles Dickens

"What has ever got your precious father, then?," said Mrs. Cratchit. "And your brother, Tiny Tim; and Martha warn't as late last Christmas Day by half-an-hour!"

"Here's Martha, mother!" cried the two young Cratchits. "Hurrah! There's *such* a goose, Martha!"

"Why, bless your heart alive, my dear, how late you are!" said Mrs. Cratchit, kissing her a dozen times, and taking off
5   her shawl and bonnet for her, with officious zeal.

"We'd a deal of work to finish up last night," replied the girl, "and had to clear away this morning, mother!"

"Well! Never mind so long as you are come," said Mrs. Cratchit. "Sit ye down before the fire, my dear, and have a warm, Lord bless ye!"

"No, no! There's father coming," cried the two young Cratchits, who were everywhere at once. "Hide, Martha, hide!"

10   So Martha hid herself, and in came little Bob, the father, with at least three feet of comforter exclusive of the fringe, hanging down before him; and his thread-bare clothes darned up and brushed, to look seasonable; and Tiny Tim upon his shoulder. Alas for Tiny Tim, he bore a little crutch, and had limbs supported by an iron frame!

"Why, where's our Martha?" cried Bob Cratchit looking round.

"Not coming," said Mrs. Cratchit.

15   "Not coming!" said Bob, with a sudden **declension** in his high spirits; for he had been Tim's blood horse all the way from church, and had come home rampant. "Not coming upon Christmas Day!"

Martha didn't like to see him disappointed, if it were only in joke; so she came out prematurely from behind the closet door, and ran into his arms, while the two young Cratchits hustled Tiny Tim, and bore him off into the wash-house, that he might hear the pudding singing in the copper.

20   "And how did little Tim behave?" asked Mrs. Cratchit, when she had rallied Bob on his credulity and Bob had hugged his daughter to his heart's content.

"As good as gold," said Bob, "and better. Somehow, he gets thoughtful sitting by himself so much, and thinks the strangest things you ever heard. He told me, coming home, that he hoped the people saw him in the church, because he was a cripple, and it might be pleasant to them to remember upon Christmas Day, who made lame
25   beggars walk and blind men see."

Bob's voice was tremulous when he told them this, and trembled more when he said that Tiny Tim was growing strong and hearty.

declension: lowering, falling

1 How do I make a critical judgement?

Before you plan your written response, you need to make a **critical judgement** on the topic in the question. This means weighing up the key evidence in the novel and coming to a conclusion: a sentence or two that sums up your ideas.

(1) One way to begin developing your critical judgement is to focus on the extract you are given in the question. Look at the exam-style question and section from Extract A on page 34.

Exam-style question

Starting with this extract, how does Dickens present families in *A Christmas Carol?*

"Why, where's our Martha?" cried Bob Cratchit looking round.

"Not coming," said Mrs. Cratchit.

"Not coming!" said Bob, with a sudden declension in his high spirits; for he had been Tim's blood horse all the way from church, and had come home rampant. "Not coming upon Christmas Day!"

playful – Martha is hiding

(a) Explore each aspect of the focus given in the question: in this case, the different members of the Cratchit family and their relationships. Annotate 🖉 the extract above with your impressions of Bob Cratchit and his children.

(b) Write 🖉 **one** or **two** sentences summing up your **critical judgement** on how families are presented **in the extract on page 34**.

....

....

(2) Now you need to think about how the theme of families is explored **in the novel as a whole**. Look at these other events in the novel in which families are shown.

| Chapter 1: Scrooge refuses to spend Christmas with Fred. | Chapter 2: Young Scrooge is not allowed to go home for Christmas. | Chapter 3: Fred, his wife and friends enjoy Christmas. | Chapter 5: Scrooge spends Christmas with Fred. |

(a) Which of these key events could be used as evidence to **support** or **develop** the critical judgement that you made in (1) (b)? Tick ✓ them.

(b) Which of these scenes **contradict** the critical judgement that you made? Cross ✗ them.

(c) Is your critical judgement on how Dickens presents families in *A Christmas Carol* still valid? Or do you need to rethink it now that you have considered other key events from the novel as a whole? Either tick ✓ your answer to (1) (b), or rewrite 🖉 it below.

....

....

2 How do I gather relevant points?

You need to gather a range of points from the extract and from the whole novel to support and develop the critical judgement you make in response to the exam question.

1 Think about how families are presented **in the extract** on page 34 and **in the whole novel**.

a Look at some different critical judgements about the presentation of families in *A Christmas Carol*. For each one, circle Ⓐ the number on the scale to show how strongly you agree or disagree.

		Disagree	Unsure	Agree
A	Families are a source of happiness and contentment.	1	2	3
B	Family is more important than anything else.	1	2	3
C	The reader responds negatively to characters who do not value their family.	1	2	3
D	The reader sympathises with characters who are not valued by their family.	1	2	3
E	Scrooge is redeemed when he recognises the importance of family.	1	2	3

b Now look at some of the key events from the novel below. Select key events that support each of the judgements that you agreed with, labelling 🖉 them **A, B, C**, etc. to show which judgement they support. Some chapters may support more than one judgement.

Chapter 1 | a Scrooge refuses to spend Christmas with Fred. |

Chapter 2 | a Young Scrooge is not allowed to go home for Christmas. |

b Fezziwig, his family, friends and neighbours celebrate Christmas. |

c Scrooge cannot bear to see the vision of Belle and her happy family. |

Chapter 3 | a The Cratchits enjoy Christmas despite their poverty. |

b Fred and his wife enjoy Christmas. |

Chapter 4 | a Scrooge dies alone. |

Chapter 5 | a Scrooge buys the Cratchits a turkey and promises to help them. |

b Scrooge spends Christmas with Fred. |

2 a Review all of your answers on this page so far. Use them to note 🖉 down in the table **three** key points you might make in your response to the exam-style question.

b For each key point, note 🖉 the key events from the novel that you could refer to as **evidence** to support your point.

	Key point	Evidence
1		
2		
3		

How do I sequence my points?

You need to sequence your key points to build a logical argument that supports your critical judgement. You need to start with the extract – but where do you go from there?

Look at this exam-style question, and one student's critical judgement in response to it.

Exam-style question

Starting with this extract, how does Dickens present families in *A Christmas Carol*?

Dickens presents families as the most important thing in our lives. Scrooge is only redeemed when he rejoins his family for Christmas and supports the Cratchit family.

Now look at these four key points, taken from the same student's plan.

A
Scrooge refuses to spend Christmas with Fred.

B
Fezziwig's Christmas celebrations.

C
Scrooge dies alone and unmourned.

D
Scrooge spends Christmas with Fred.

(1) One way to sequence the key points in a response is to work your way through the novel **chronologically**: exploring how a character or theme develops as the story progresses.

How would you sequence the four key points above if you were organising this response **chronologically**? Write 🖉 the letters **A–D** in the order in which you would sequence them.

☐ ☐ ☐ ☐

(2) Another way to organise the key points in a response is to **synthesise** your key points: grouping related points together.

For example, you could:

(a) group your key points by **character**. ☐

How would you sequence the key points above if you were going to explore how Dickens presents the family of one **character** and then another? Write 🖉 the letters **A–D**.

☐ ☐ ☐ ☐

Or you could:

(b) group your key points by **approach**. ☐

How would you sequence the key points above if you were going to look at one way in which Dickens presents family, and then another way in which Dickens presents family? 🖉

☐ ☐ ☐ ☐

(3) Look at all of your answers above.

(a) Which method would **you** choose to sequence the key points above? Tick ✓ it.

(b) Write 🖉 **one** or **two** sentences explaining your choice.

....

....

Planning your response

To plan an effective response, you need to:

- make a critical judgement summing up your response to the focus of the question
- gather relevant points: identify the key events in the novel that support your critical judgement and use them to develop points you can make in your response
- sequence your points: decide on the most effective way to build a logical argument that supports your critical judgement: for example, chronologically, or by character, or by approach.

Look at this exam-style question you saw at the start of the unit.

Exam-style question

Starting with this extract, how does Dickens present families in *A Christmas Carol*?

Write about:

- how Dickens presents families in this extract
- how Dickens presents families in the novel as a whole.

(1) Now look at these two paragraphs, written by a student in response to the exam-style question above.

> In 'A Christmas Carol', Dickens shows that ignoring your family leads to unhappiness. In Chapter 2, Scrooge sobs at the sight of his younger self left at school over the Christmas holidays because his father would not allow him to come home. This shows the dramatic effect that being kept apart from your family can have.
>
> However, Scrooge goes on to make the same mistake in his own life, rejecting his own family. At the beginning of the novel, Scrooge refuses to go to his nephew's house for Christmas. This shows that the miserable, isolated old miser does not recognise the importance of family until later in the novel when the Ghost of Christmas Yet To Come shows Scrooge his own death. The Ghost shows Scrooge that, unless he changes his ways, he will die alone, no one will mourn him and the poor will help themselves to his possessions. Soon after, Scrooge decides he will celebrate Christmas with his nephew, suggesting that it is this vision that most strongly persuades Scrooge to change his attitude to his family and to Christmas.

a Write ✏ **one** sentence summarising the critical judgement that these paragraphs support.

....

....

b Circle Ⓐ all the evidence of key events in the novel used in these paragraphs to support the critical response.

c How has this student organised their key points? Tick ✓ **one**.

  A chronologically ⬚

  B by character ⬚

  C by approach ⬚

Your turn!

You are now going to **plan and write your own answer** in response to the exam-style question.

> **Exam-style question**
>
> Starting with this extract, how does Dickens present families in *A Christmas Carol*?
>
> Write about:
> - how Dickens presents families in this extract
> - how Dickens presents families in the novel as a whole.
>
> (30 marks)

1. Sum up ✐ your **critical judgement** in response to the exam-style question above. This will be the **conclusion** that your response must support.

   ....

   ....

   ....

2. Which **key events** in the novel will you explore in your response to support your critical judgement? Note ✐ them below.

3. Note ✐ down all the **key points** you will make about these key events to support your critical judgement.

   ....

   ....

   ....

   ....

4. a How will you sequence your key points? Tick ✓ **one** answer.

   chronologically ☐   by character ☐   by approach ☐

   b Number ✐ your key points in ③, sequencing them to build an argument that supports your critical judgement.

5. Now write ✐ your response on paper to the exam-style question above.

Review your skills

Check up

Review your response to the exam-style question on page 39. Tick ✓ the column to show how well you think you have done each of the following.

	Not quite ✓	Nearly there ✓	Got it! ✓
made a critical judgement	☐	☐	☐
made key points using key events in the novel to support my critical judgement	☐	☐	☐
sequenced my key points to build an argument that supports my critical judgement	☐	☐	☐

Look over all of your work in this unit. Note ✐ down the **three** most important things to remember when planning your response.

1. ....

2. ....

3. ....

Need more practice?

Here is another exam-style question, this time relating to the extract from Chapter 3 on page 75 (Extract C).

Exam-style question

Starting with this extract, how does Dickens present the people of Victorian Britain in *A Christmas Carol*?

Write about:

• how Dickens presents Victorian Britain in this extract

• how Dickens presents Victorian Britain in the novel as a whole. (30 marks)

Plan ✐ your response to this question. Aim to:

• sum up your critical judgement in one or two sentences

• identify key events to focus on, and key points to make

• sequence your ideas.

You'll find some suggested ideas in the Answers section.

How confident do you feel about each of these **skills?** Colour ✐ in the bars.

❶ How do I make a critical judgement?	❷ How do I gather relevant points?	❸ How do I sequence my points?

Read, understand and respond to texts (AO1); Analyse the language, form and structure used by a writer to create meanings and effects (AO2)

6 Writing your response

This unit will help you write the part of your response in which you have to focus on **the novel as a whole**. The skills you will build are to:

- know key events and key quotations you can use when writing about the novel as a whole
- understand how to use key events and quotations as evidence
- be able to analyse evidence from the novel effectively.

In the exam you will face a question like the one below. This is about the extract on the next page. At the end of the unit you will **write your own response** to the **second part** of this question.

Reminder: For more help on writing about **the extract**, see Units 2 and 3.

Exam-style question

Starting with this extract, how does Dickens present kindness and generosity in *A Christmas Carol?*

Write about:

- how Dickens presents kindness and generosity in the novel
- how Dickens presents kindness and generosity in the novel as a whole.

(30 marks)

Before you tackle the question you will work through three key questions in the **skills boosts** to help you write your response.

1 How do I choose key events and key quotations to learn?

2 How do I use evidence to support my ideas?

3 How do I analyse my evidence?

Read the extract on the next page from Chapter 3 of *A Christmas Carol*.

As you read, think about the following: ⊘

What has happened before this extract? What happens after this extract?

How does Dickens present Fred and his wife's attitude to Scrooge?

How does Dickens show Fred's kindness and generosity in this extract?

Read the following extract from Chapter 3 of *A Christmas Carol*.

In this extract the Ghost of Christmas Present is showing Scrooge a vision of Christmas at his nephew Fred's house.

Extract A | Chapter 3 of *A Christmas Carol* by Charles Dickens

"He's a comical old fellow," said Scrooge's nephew, "that's the truth; and not so pleasant as he might be. However, his offences carry their own punishment, and I have nothing to say against him."

"I'm sure he is very rich, Fred," hinted Scrooge's niece. "At least you always tell *me* so."

"What of that, my dear!" said Scrooge's nephew. "His wealth is of no use to him. He don't do any good with it. He
5 don't make himself comfortable with it. He hasn't the satisfaction of thinking – ha, ha, ha! – that he is ever going to benefit Us with it."

"I have no patience with him," observed Scrooge's niece. Scrooge's niece's sisters, and all the other ladies, expressed the same opinion.

"Oh, I have!" said Scrooge's nephew. "I am sorry for him; I couldn't be angry with him if I tried. Who suffers by his ill
10 whims? Himself, always. Here, he takes it into his head to dislike us, and he won't come and dine with us. What's the consequence? He don't lose much of a dinner."

"Indeed, I think he loses a very good dinner," interrupted Scrooge's niece. Everybody else said the same, and they must be allowed to have been competent judges, because they had just had dinner; and, with the dessert upon the table, were clustered round the fire, by lamplight.

15 "Well! I'm very glad to hear it," said Scrooge's nephew, "because I haven't great faith in these young housekeepers. What do *you* say, Topper?"

Topper had clearly got his eye upon one of Scrooge's niece's sisters, for he answered that a bachelor was a wretched outcast, who had no right to express an opinion on the subject. Whereat Scrooge's niece's sister – the plump one with the lace tucker: not the one with the roses – blushed.

20 "Do go on, Fred," said Scrooge's niece, clapping her hands. "He never finishes what he begins to say! He is such a ridiculous fellow!"

Scrooge's nephew revelled in another laugh, and as it was impossible to keep the infection off; though the plump sister tried hard to do it with aromatic vinegar; his example was unanimously followed.

"I was only going to say," said Scrooge's nephew, "that the consequence of his taking a dislike to us, and not making
25 merry with us, is, as I think, that he loses some pleasant moments, which could do him no harm. I am sure he loses pleasanter companions than he can find in his own thoughts, either in his mouldy old office, or his dusty chambers. I mean to give him the same chance every year, whether he likes it or not, for I pity him. He may rail at Christmas till he dies, but he can't help thinking better of it – I defy him – if he finds me going there, in good temper, year after year, and saying Uncle Scrooge, how are you? If it only puts him in the vein to leave his poor clerk fifty pounds,
30 *that's* something; and I think I shook him, yesterday."

It was their turn to laugh now, at the notion of his shaking Scrooge. But being thoroughly good-natured, and not much caring what they laughed at, so that they laughed at any rate, he encouraged them in their merriment, and passed the bottle, joyously.

How do I choose key events and key quotations to learn?

When you write about the **extract**, you should support your response with quotations from the extract. When you write about the **novel as a whole**, you should refer to key events. You can also use some key quotations that you have learned to show your detailed understanding of the novel.

Reminder: For more help on writing about the **extract**, see Units 2 and 3.

The key events in the novel are those which: show a significant aspect of, or development in, a key character **or** explore a key theme.

(1) Look at the extract on page 42 (Extract A). Which of the key characters and themes below are significant in this part of Chapter 3? Circle (A) them.

Characters
- Scrooge
- Fred
- Bob Cratchit
- Jacob Marley
- Ghosts of Christmas

Themes
- poverty and greed
- Christmas
- family
- generosity
- the supernatural

Think about who is talking – and who or what they are talking about.

(2) Now look at some of the other events in Chapter 3.

A | Ghost of Christmas Past appears. ☐

B | A vision of the people of London on Christmas morning. ☐

C | A vision of the Cratchits' house at Christmas. ☐

D | Visions of miners, lighthouse-keepers and sailors enjoying Christmas. ☐

(a) Which events reveal something about a key character? Label (✎) them with that character's name.

(b) Which explore a key theme? Label (✎) them with the name of that theme.

(c) Review your answers to questions (1) and (2). Which key events in Chapter 3 should you make sure you know? Tick (✓) them.

(3) The best quotations to learn are short, and can be used to support two (or more) different ideas.

A | "I will honour Christmas in my heart, and try to keep it all the year." (Chapter 4) ☐

B | "I am as merry as a school-boy." (Chapter 5) ☐

C | "A merry Christmas, Bob!" (Chapter 5) ☐

D | And to Tiny Tim, who did NOT die, he was a second father. (Chapter 5) ☐

(a) Which quotation most effectively shows Scrooge's kindness and generosity **and** reveals something about a key theme of the novel? Tick (✓) **one**.

(b) Look at the quotation you have chosen. How could you make it shorter and easier to learn off by heart? Underline (A) the most significant or revealing phrase of five words or fewer.

2 How do I use evidence to support my ideas?

You can use **key events** in the novel and **key quotations** as evidence to **support** and **explain** your ideas.

Look at one student's **key idea**, or **critical judgement**, in response to this exam question.

Exam-style question

Starting with this extract, how does Dickens present kindness and generosity in *A Christmas Carol*?

All the key characters are kind and generous, except Scrooge, who is redeemed when he shows kindness and generosity.

(1) Look again at Extract A on page 42. Note 🖉 down **one key event** and **one key quotation** from this part of the novel to support the student's **key idea**.

Key event: ....

Key quotation: ....

(2) Now think about **key events** elsewhere in the novel. Which would support the key idea above?

Note 🖉 down **two** key events.

Hint: Think about:
- what Scrooge **says** and **does**
- what Scrooge **sees** and **hears** other characters doing.

1 ....

2 ....

....

(3) Which **key quotations** from the novel would support the key idea above? Tick ✓ **any** of the quotes below, or note 🖉 your own on paper.

A
"Are there no prisons?"
(Scrooge, Chapter 1)

B
"I don't make merry myself at Christmas, and I can't afford to make idle people merry."
(Scrooge, Chapter 1)

C
"I wear the chain I forged in life"
(Marley, Chapter 1)

D
"No rest, no peace. Incessant torture of remorse."
(Marley, Chapter 1)

E
"Father is so much kinder than he used to be, that home's like Heaven!"
(Fan, Chapter 2)

F
"I should like to be able to say a word or two to my clerk just now!"
(Scrooge, Chapter 2)

G
"What Idol has displaced you?" …
"A golden one."
(Scrooge and Belle, Chapter 2)

H
"I'll give you Mr. Scrooge, the Founder of the Feast."
(Bob Cratchit, Chapter 3)

I
"tell me if Tiny Tim will live"
(Scrooge, Chapter 3)

J
"Are these the shadows of the things that Will be, or are they shadows of things that May be, only?"
(Scrooge, Chapter 4)

(4) Review the evidence you have gathered above. Which supports the key idea at the top of this page more effectively? ✓

☐ the key events you noted in (2)?   ☐ the quotations you selected in (3)?   ☐ or both?

How do I analyse my evidence?

Every key **idea or point** you make should be supported with **evidence** which you can **analyse**, exploring the effect of the writer's choices of language and structure, what it suggests about theme and character, and its impact on the audience.

Look at one student's key idea, or **critical judgement**, on the theme of kindness and generosity in *A Christmas Carol*.

> All the key characters are kind and generous, except Scrooge, who is redeemed when he shows kindness and generosity.

Now look at a **key quotation** you could use as evidence to support this key idea.

> As the Cratchit family sit down to eat their Christmas dinner, Bob Cratchit says, '"I'll give you Mr. Scrooge, the Founder of the (Feast)."'

To develop an effective analysis, think about these **five areas** of analysis:

A **Explain the evidence in the context of the whole story:** Why does Bob Cratchit say this?

> Despite his treatment by Scrooge, and their poor dinner, Cratchit is still grateful. ☐

B **Think about language and structure:** What does the word 'Feast' suggest?

> 'Feast' suggests a huge banquet – which could either be ironic or show how grateful he is. ☐

C **Think about character:** What does this suggest about Cratchit's character?

> He is kind, generous and forgiving: the opposite of Scrooge. ☐

D **Think about theme:** What does this suggest about the theme of kindness and generosity?

> Poverty does not stop Cratchit being kind and generous. ☐

E **Think about Dickens' intention:** How does the writer want the reader to respond?

> Cratchit's attitude makes Scrooge seem even more hard-hearted. ☐

(1) Look at one student's ideas for analysis of the **key quotation** above. Which ideas would you include in your analysis of this quote? Tick ✓ them.

(2) Now look at a key event that you could use as evidence to support the key idea above.

> In Chapter 5, Scrooge buys a huge turkey to give to the Cratchit family.

Use the **five areas of analysis** above to help you note 🖊 some ideas you could use in your analysis of this key event. Continue on paper if necessary.

Writing your response

To write an effective response, you should:

- be familiar with the key events of the novel
- know some key quotations from the novel off by heart
- use key events and key quotations as evidence to support your ideas about the novel's key themes and characters
- analyse your evidence, thinking about language, structure, theme, character and Dickens' intention.

Look at this exam-style question you saw on page 41.

Exam-style question

Starting with this extract, how does Dickens present kindness and generosity in *A Christmas Carol?*

Write about:

- how Dickens presents kindness and generosity in this extract
- how Dickens presents kindness and generosity in the novel as a whole.

Now look at a paragraph focusing on the novel as a whole, taken from one student's response to the question.

At the start of the story, Scrooge is shown to be mean and cruel. For example, he grudgingly allows Bob Cratchit just one day's holiday at Christmas and refuses to give money to a gentleman who is collecting for the poor and needy so they can have food and warmth at Christmas. Scrooge tells him that he '"can't afford to make idle people merry"'. The word 'idle' suggests that Scrooge thinks the poor are poor because they are lazy and will not work. His rejection of this opportunity to be kind and generous shows how hard-hearted and cold Scrooge is, making the reader feel angry and unsympathetic towards him. However, as the story progresses, Scrooge comes to understand the rewards that kindness and generosity can bring.

- uses a key event as evidence
- uses a quotation as evidence
- explains the context of the evidence
- analysis comment on the writer's choices of language and/or structure
- analysis comment on character
- analysis comment on theme
- analysis comment on Dickens' intention

(1) Can you identify all the different things the student has included in this paragraph?
Link 🖉 the annotations to the paragraph to show where the student has included them.

Your turn!

You are now going to **write your own answer** in response to the exam-style question.

Starting with this extract, how does Dickens present kindness and generosity in *A Christmas Carol*?

Write about:

- how Dickens presents kindness and generosity in this extract
- how Dickens presents kindness and generosity in the novel as a whole.

(30 marks)

(1) Write ✏ **one** or **two** sentences summarising your critical judgement in response to the question.

....

....

(2) Which key events in the novel would support your critical judgement? Note ✏ them below.

Evidence

(3) Which quotations could you explore in your response? Add ✏ them above.

(4) Look at all the evidence you have gathered. Think about:
- language and structure in your quotations
- what your evidence suggests about key characters
- what your evidence suggests about the theme you are exploring: kindness and generosity
- what your evidence suggests about Dickens' intention: how might the reader respond at this point?

Annotate ✏ your evidence with your ideas.

(5) Look at your annotated evidence.

   a Which are your strongest ideas? Tick ✓ them.

   b Number ✏ the ideas that you have ticked, sequencing them to build an argument that supports your critical judgement.

(6) Now write ✏ your response to the exam-style question above on paper.

Review your skills

Check up

Review your response to the exam-style question on page 47. Tick ✓ the column to show how well you think you have done each of the following.

	Not quite ✓	Nearly there ✓	Got it! ✓
selected relevant key events to support my critical judgement	☐	☐	☐
selected relevant key quotations to support my critical judgement	☐	☐	☐
analysed my evidence effectively	☐	☐	☐

Look over all of your work in this unit. Note 🖉 down the **three** most important things to remember when writing your response.

1. ....

2. ....

3. ....

Need more practice?

Here is another exam-style question, this time relating to the extract from Chapter 3 of *A Christmas Carol* on page 75 (Extract C).

Exam-style question

Starting with this extract, how does Dickens present the people of Victorian Britain in *A Christmas Carol*?

Write about:

• how Dickens presents Victorian Britain in this extract

• how Dickens presents Victorian Britain in the novel as a whole.

(30 marks)

Write 🖉 your response to this question.

You'll find some suggested points to refer to in the Answers section.

How confident do you feel about each of these **skills?** Colour 🖉 in the bars.

1 How do I choose key events and key quotations to learn?	2 How do I use evidence to support my ideas?	3 How do I analyse my evidence?

Analyse the language, form and structure used by a writer to create meanings and effects (AO2)

⑦ Commenting on structure

This unit will help you to comment on Dickens' structural choices in *A Christmas Carol*. The skills you will build are to:

- identify significant structural features of the novel
- explore the impact of some of the structural features of the novel, including setting
- build comments on the novel's structure into your analysis.

In the exam you will face a question like the one below. This is about the extract on the next page. At the end of the unit you will **write your own response** to this question.

Exam-style question

Starting with this extract, how does Dickens present justice and fairness in *A Christmas Carol*?

Write about:

- how Dickens presents justice and fairness in this extract
- how Dickens presents justice and fairness in the novel as a whole.

(30 marks)

Before you tackle the question you will work through three key questions in the **skills boosts** to help you comment on the structure of the novel.

① How can I comment on the settings in the novel? > **② How do I comment on the structure of the novel?** > **③ How do I analyse the writer's use of structure?**

Read the extract on the next page from Chapter 3 of *A Christmas Carol*.

As you read, think about the following:

 What has happened before this extract? What happens after this extract?

 Why has Dickens chosen to position this vision at this point in the novel?

 What does the description of Ignorance and Want suggest about justice and fairness in Victorian Britain?

Read the following extract from Chapter 3 of *A Christmas Carol*.

In this extract the Ghost of Christmas Present shows Scrooge a vision of two children: Ignorance and Want.

Extract A | Chapter 3 of *A Christmas Carol* by Charles Dickens

From the foldings of its robe, it brought two children; wretched, abject, frightful, hideous, miserable. They knelt down at its feet, and clung upon the outside of its garment.

"Oh, Man! look here. Look, look, down here!" exclaimed the Ghost.

5 They were a boy and girl. Yellow, meagre, ragged, scowling, wolfish; but prostrate, too, in their humility. Where graceful youth should have filled their features out, and touched them with its freshest tints, a stale and shrivelled hand, like that of age, had pinched, and twisted them, and pulled them into shreds. Where angels might have sat enthroned, devils lurked, and glared out menacing. No change, no degradation, no perversion of humanity, in any grade, through all the mysteries of wonderful creation, has monsters half so horrible and dread.

Scrooge started back, appalled. Having them shown to him in this way, he tried to say they were fine children, but
10 the words choked themselves, rather than be parties to a lie of such enormous magnitude.

"Spirit! are they yours?" Scrooge could say no more.

"They are Man's," said the Spirit, looking down upon them. "And they cling to me, appealing from their fathers. This boy is Ignorance. This girl is Want. Beware them both, and all of their degree, but most of all beware this boy, for on his brow I see that written which is Doom, unless the writing be erased. Deny it!" cried the Spirit, stretching out
15 its hand towards the city. "Slander those who tell it ye! Admit it for your factious purposes, and make it worse! And bide the end!"

"Have they no refuge or resource?" cried Scrooge.

"Are there no prisons?" said the Spirit, turning on him for the last time with his own words. "Are there no workhouses?"

20 The bell struck twelve.

Scrooge looked about him for the Ghost, and saw it not. As the last stroke ceased to vibrate, he remembered the prediction of old Jacob Marley, and lifting up his eyes, beheld a solemn Phantom, draped and hooded, coming, like a mist along the ground, towards him.

How can I comment on the settings in the novel?

The settings in *A Christmas Carol* help Dickens to develop the reader's understanding of his characters and the ideas he wants to explore.

1 Look at some key quotations from the extract on page 50 (Extract A). What do they suggest about the setting (Victorian Britain) of the novel?

> a stale and shrivelled hand, like that of age, had pinched, and twisted them, and pulled them into shreds.

> "They are Man's," said the Spirit,

> "… This boy is Ignorance. This girl is Want …"

> "Are there no prisons?" said the Spirit | "Are there no workhouses?"

Write 🖉 **one** or **two** sentences, summing up your ideas.

....

....

....

2 There is a wide variety of settings within the novel. Each one reflects the characters who live there and reveals something about them.

A **Fezziwig's**
> There were more dances and | there was cake, and there was negus

B **The streets of London**
> The house fronts looked black enough | the windows blacker | the people | were jovial and full of glee

C **The Cratchits' home**
> they were not well dressed; their shoes were far from being water-proof | But, they were happy, grateful

D **Fred's home**
> a bright, dry, gleaming room | Scrooge's niece played well upon the harp

E **A miner's hut**
> Passing through the wall of mud and stone, they found a cheerful company assembled round a glowing fire.

Complete 🖉 the sentences below, thinking about similarities and differences in these settings and their characters.

> Think about what they are doing, and what each setting reveals about them.

a In all of the settings, everyone is ....

b Settings A and D are similar because ....

c However, settings B, C and E are different because ....

3 In what ways are all the settings above, and the people in them, similar to and different from Scrooge and his setting? Write 🖉 **one** or **two** sentences explaining your ideas.

Scrooge
> a small fire in the grate; spoon and basin ready; and the little saucepan of gruel | upon the hob

....

....

2 How do I comment on the structure of the novel?

A *Christmas Carol* is structured in five chapters, or *staves*. Dickens uses this structure to show the transformation of Scrooge and control the reader's response to it.

1 Think about how Dickens has structured the novel to manipulate his readers. Add some or all of the words below, and/or some of your own ideas, to the flow chart beneath.

> You may want to use some words more than once.

Scrooge's	coldness	meanness	spirits	past	present	future

visions	hardship	suffering	isolation	generosity	kindness	transformation

Beginning: Chapter 1

Dickens engages the reader's attention with ....

Middle: Chapters 2–4

Dickens holds the reader's attention with ....

End: Chapter 5

Dickens creates a satisfying ending for the reader with ....

2 Chapters 2, 3 and 4 are structured around the visions of the Past, Present and Future.

Visions of the Past

Scrooge's childhood, apprenticeship and broken engagement.

Visions of the Present

Christmas Day in the streets of London, at the Cratchits', and at Fred's.

Visions of the Future

Scrooge and Tiny Tim are dead.

Use the sentence fragments below to help you summarise what each Ghost shows Scrooge and the reader.

The Ghost of Christmas Past	The Ghost of Christmas Present	The Ghost of Christmas Yet To Come

shows Scrooge and the reader	the causes of	the consequences of	the importance of	the contrast of

Scrooge's	unhappiness	love of money	isolation	Christmas

poverty and wealth	kindness and generosity

How do I analyse the writer's use of structure?

You can build effective comments on structure into your analysis of the novel. Think about how a key event develops or contrasts with other key events, and its impact on the reader.

Look at some sentences taken from one student's response to an exam-style question.

Exam-style question

How does Dickens present justice and fairness in *A Christmas Carol*?

> Dickens ends Chapter 3 with a shocking vision of two children: Ignorance and Want. The Ghost of Christmas Present taunts Scrooge with his own words: '"Are there no prisons? ... Are there no workhouses?"', highlighting the cruel and unfair ways in which Victorian society treated the poor.

(1) Now look at some sentences focusing on the novel's structure that could be added to this paragraph.

A
> This follows visions of a poor Christmas at the Cratchits' and a rich Christmas at Fred's.

B
> This sudden change from the happiness of Christmas creates a dramatic end to Chapter 3, persuading Scrooge and the reader to help the poor.

C
> Dickens contrasts Victorian society's wealth and poverty to emphasise its unfairness.

D
> Scrooge's reaction shows how much he has changed since the start of the novel.

(a) Which sentences would you add to the student's response paragraph above? Tick ✓ them.

(b) Mark ✐ where you would add them by writing the letter **A, B, C, D** on the student's response paragraph above.

(2) Now look at another paragraph taken from the same student's response.

> Another way in which Dickens presents justice is when Scrooge is dead. The Ghost of Christmas Yet To Come shows him rich men who will not go to his funeral and poor people stealing his belongings. This seems like justice because Scrooge did not care about other people when he was alive, and now no one cares about him.

Write ✐ **one** or **two** sentences that could be added to this paragraph, to develop the analysis by focusing on the novel's structure.

You could comment on:

- how this vision of the future contrasts with the vision of the present seen in Chapter 3
- the impact on Scrooge and the reader of this vision at this point in the story.

....

....

....

Commenting on structure

To comment on the structure of the novel, you need to:

- identify significant structural choices that Dickens has made
- consider how Dickens has used these structural choices to manipulate the reader's response to the characters and events in the novel
- link these structural features and their impact to the focus of the question.

Look at this exam-style question you saw at the start of the unit.

Exam-style question

Starting with this extract, how does Dickens present justice and fairness in *A Christmas Carol*?

Write about:

- how Dickens presents justice and fairness in this extract
- how Dickens presents justice and fairness in the novel as a whole.

Now look at a paragraph taken from one student's response to the question.

Although the story shows that Victorian society is not fair or equal, it also shows that the rich who care only about themselves will eventually be brought to justice and punished. This is the first lesson that Scrooge must learn in the novel when he is visited by the Ghost of Jacob Marley. Marley is bound in a huge, heavy chain, which he says is the chain that he 'forged in life', and is doomed to wander the earth, suggesting that he is being punished in the afterlife for his actions when he was alive. By positioning Marley's visit at the start of the novel, Dickens makes it clear to Scrooge and to the reader that he will face the same justice if he does not change his ways. This helps to engage the reader, but it is also a warning that we should all think about justice and fairness and pay close attention to what the other spirits will show us.

(1) What is the significant structural choice that the student explores in this paragraph? ✏

....

....

....

(2) Identify the part of the paragraph in which the student comments on how Dickens has used this structural choice to manipulate the reader's response. Underline (A) it and label (✏) it **'intention'**.

(3) Identify the part of the paragraph in which the student links this structural feature and its impact to the focus of the question. Underline (A) it and label (✏) it **'question'**.

Your turn!

You are now going to **write your own answer** in response to the exam-style question.

Exam-style question

Starting with this extract, how does Dickens present justice and fairness in *A Christmas Carol*?

Write about:

- how Dickens presents justice and fairness in this extract
- how Dickens presents justice and fairness in the novel as a whole.

(30 marks)

① Write 🖉 **one** or **two** sentences summarising your critical judgement in response to the question.

....

....

② Which key events and/or quotations would support your critical judgement? Note 🖉 them below.

Evidence

③ Look at all the evidence you have gathered. Think about how you could use it to comment on:

- **language and structure** in your quotations
- **character**
- the **theme** you are exploring: justice and fairness
- the **structure** of the novel
- Dickens' **intention**: how might the reader respond?

Annotate 🖉 your evidence with your ideas.

④ Look at your annotated evidence.

a Which are your strongest ideas? Tick ✓ them.

b Number 🖉 the ideas that you have ticked and sequence them here to build an argument that supports your critical judgement.

⑤ Now write 🖉 your response to the exam-style question above on paper.

Review your skills

Check up

Review your response to the exam-style question on page 55. Tick ✓ the column to show how well you think you have done each of the following.

	Not quite ✓	Nearly there ✓	Got it! ✓
selected relevant evidence, commenting on character and theme	☐	☐	☐
identified relevant and significant structural features of the novel	☐	☐	☐
commented on the impact of those structural features	☐	☐	☐
linked my comments on structure to the focus of the question	☐	☐	☐

Look over all of your work in this unit. Note 🖉 down the **three** most important things to remember when commenting on the structure of the novel.

1. ....

2. ....

3. ....

Need more practice?

Look at this exam-style question, this time relating to the extract from Chapter 3 of *A Christmas Carol* on page 76 (Extract D).

Exam-style question

Starting with this extract, how does Dickens present choices and consequences in *A Christmas Carol*? Write about:

• how Dickens presents choices and consequences in this extract

• how Dickens presents choices and consequences in the novel as a whole.   **(30 marks)**

Plan 🖉 your response to the question.

• Which key events will you focus on? Note them down.

• Which key structural features of the novel will you focus on? Add them to your plan.

• What impact do these structural features have on the presentation of choices and consequences in *A Christmas Carol*? Note your ideas.

You'll find some suggested ideas in the Answers section.

How confident do you feel about each of these **skills?** Colour 🖉 in the bars.

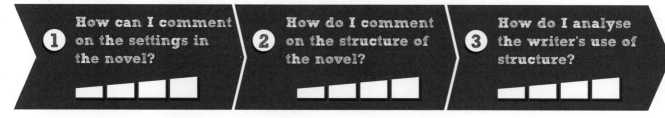

1 How can I comment on the settings in the novel?   2 How do I comment on the structure of the novel?   3 How do I analyse the writer's use of structure?

(8) Commenting on context

This unit will help you to show your understanding of the novel's context: its relationship with the time the novel was written. The skills you will build are to:

- understand the relationship between the novel and its context
- explain the impact of context on different elements of the novel
- incorporate comments on context into your writing about the novel.

In the exam you will face a question like the one below. This is about the extract on the next page. At the end of the unit you will **write your own response** to this question.

Exam-style question

Starting with this extract, how does Dickens present the poor in *A Christmas Carol*?

Write about:

- how Dickens presents the poor in this extract
- how Dickens presents the poor in the novel as a whole.

(30 marks)

Before you tackle the question you will work through three key questions in the **skills boosts** to help you write about the novel's context.

 1 How do I know which contextual ideas to write about?

 2 How do I comment on context?

 3 How do I build my comments on context into my analysis?

Read the extract on the next page from Chapter 4 of *A Christmas Carol*.

As you read, think about the following:

What has happened before this extract? What happens after this extract? ☐	What does the extract suggest about the Cratchit family? ☐	What does the extract suggest about the Cratchits' poverty? ☐

Read the following extract from Chapter 4 of *A Christmas Carol*.

In this extract the Ghost of Christmas Yet To Come shows Scrooge a vision of the Cratchits' house.

Extract A | Chapter 4 of *A Christmas Carol* by Charles Dickens

The mother laid her work upon the table, and put her hand up to her face.

"The colour hurts my eyes," she said.

The colour? Ah, poor Tiny Tim!

"They're better now again," said Cratchit's wife. "It makes them weak by candle-light; and I wouldn't show weak eyes
5 to your father when he comes home, for the world. It must be near his time."

"Past it rather," Peter answered, shutting up his book.

"But I think he has walked a little slower than he used, these few last evenings, mother."

They were very quiet again. At last she said, and in a steady cheerful voice, that only faltered once:

"I have known him walk with – I have known him walk with Tiny Tim upon his shoulder, very fast indeed."

10 "And so have I," cried Peter. "Often."

"And so have I!" exclaimed another. So had all.

"But he was very light to carry," she resumed, intent upon her work, "and his father loved him so, that it was no
trouble – no trouble. And there is your father at the door!"

She hurried out to meet him; and little Bob in his comforter – he had need of it, poor fellow – came in. His tea was
15 ready for him on the hob, and they all tried who should help him to it most. Then the two young Cratchits got upon
his knees and laid, each child a little cheek, against his face, as if they said, "Don't mind it, father. Don't be grieved!"

Bob was very cheerful with them, and spoke pleasantly to all the family. He looked at the work upon the table, and
praised the industry and speed of Mrs. Cratchit and the girls. They would be done long before Sunday, he said.

"Sunday! You went to-day, then, Robert?" said his wife.

20 "Yes, my dear," returned Bob. "I wish you could have gone. It would have done you good to see how green a place
it is. But you'll see it often. I promised him that I would walk there on a Sunday. My little, little child!" cried Bob.
"My little child!"

He broke down all at once. He couldn't help it. If he could have helped it, he and his child would have been farther
apart perhaps than they were.

25 He left the room, and went up stairs into the room above, which was lighted cheerfully, and hung with Christmas.
There was a chair set close beside the child, and there were signs of some one having been there, lately. Poor Bob
sat down in it, and when he had thought a little and composed himself, he kissed the little face. He was reconciled
to what had happened, and went down again quite happy.

1 How do I know which contextual ideas to write about?

You need to be aware of all the different contexts of *A Christmas Carol* on which you could comment so that you can choose those that are relevant to your response.

(1) Look at some of the features of *A Christmas Carol* and the time in which it was written. Tick ✓ any that are relevant to the novel, and cross ✗ any that are not.

A Christmas Carol
- Written by Dickens in 1843.
- Did much to popularise the 'spirit of Christmas'.
- Set in an overcrowded, polluted London.

Christmas
- At the beginning of the 19th century, Christmas was hardly celebrated.
- Queen Victoria and Prince Albert popularised the celebration of Christmas.
- Christmas trees, cards and crackers all became popular in the 1840s.

The Family
- Victorians idealised the family and the home as a place of love, co-operation and reliability.
- Queen Victoria and Prince Albert were seen as role models: a devoted husband and wife, and loving parents to nine children.

The Industrial Revolution
- With industrialisation, thousands of workers moved from the countryside into towns and cities, leading to overcrowding.
- There was a huge gap between the rich who owned the factories and the poor who worked in them.

Charity
- It has been estimated that more than 300 charities started between 1800 and 1850.
- Contributing time and/or money to charities was seen as the social duty of any who had time and/or money to spare.
- Charities provided a free basic education, although many poor children had to work full time to help their families survive.

The New Poor Law of 1834
- The workhouse offered the only support to the unemployed poor. Clothing and food were provided in exchange for hard, physical labour. Conditions were intentionally terrible to deter any who were not desperate.

The Poor
- Living conditions for the city poor were terrible. Poor housing, overcrowding, pollution and expensive health care meant that one fifth of poor children died before their first birthday.
- It was a common Victorian attitude that the poor were poor because they wasted money on alcohol and gambling.

(2) Now think about some of these key characters in the novel.

| Scrooge | The Cratchits | Ghosts of Christmas | Ignorance and Want |

Annotate ✐ the diagram with these words, using arrows to link them to all the relevant elements of context.

② How do I comment on context?

An effective comment on the context of *A Christmas Carol* should focus on **when** the novel was written, a **relevant belief, attitude or situation** at that time, and the impact that Dickens intended to have on his **readers**.

Look at the beginning of one student's paragraph exploring how the Cratchits are presented in Extract A on page 58.

> Throughout the extract, Dickens emphasises how loving the Cratchit family are as they come to terms with the death of Tiny Tim.

(1) Now look at some different students' comments on the context of the novel in this scene.

A — Your family was thought to be very important in those days. ☐

B — The Cratchits are presented as the perfect Victorian family, showing all the things that the Victorians admired. They are hard-working, loving and respectful. ☐

C — Dickens presents this picture of a perfect but heartbroken family to create sympathy for them in his Victorian readers, who may have considered the poor to be lazy and irresponsible. ☐

a Which comment does what? Circle Ⓐ or cross out each letter in the table below.

Context	Comment		
identifies the time in which the novel was written	A	B	C
identifies a relevant belief, attitude or situation at that time	A	B	C
considers Dickens' intention	A	B	C
considers the impact on the reader	A	B	C

b Which of the comments above would you use when writing about how the Cratchit family are presented in the extract? Tick ✓ **one or more**.

(2) Look at these sentences from the beginning of another student's paragraph about Ignorance and Want.

> At the end of Chapter 3, the Ghost of Christmas Present shows Scrooge a vision of two children: Ignorance and Want. They make you feel sorry for poor children.

a Write ✏ **one** or **two** sentences adding a contextual comment to the paragraph.

Think about: Why might Dickens have wanted his readers to see the problems of ignorance and want?

....

....

b Check your comment. Does it achieve all or most of the criteria listed in question **①** **a**? Adjust ✏ it as necessary.

How do I build my comments on context into my analysis?

You do not need to make contextual comments in every paragraph of your response, but you do need to make them relevant to your analysis of the novel.

Look at a paragraph from a student's response, commenting on how Dickens presents the poor in Chapter 4 of *A Christmas Carol*.

> In Chapter 4, Dickens shows a group of poor people selling a dead man's belongings in a dirty backstreet shop. These include the shirt his corpse was dressed in and curtains that were hanging around his bed as he lay on it dead. One woman comments that it is the man's fault that they stole from him because he had no family to watch his body or mourn for him.

(1) Now look at some sentences you could add to this paragraph.

A
> This emphasises to Scrooge and to the reader that money is not the only important thing in life.

a
> It highlights the extreme poverty of the poor in the 1840s that even some curtains and a dead man's shirt were worth stealing.

B
> It shows how desperate these people are.

b
> Dickens may have intended this scene to shock Victorian readers into changing their attitude to the poor and to support charities, which many Victorians thought was the duty of the rich.

C
> Scrooge does not know who the corpse is, but realises that he treated people in the same way as this man so this helps him realise that he needs to change his ways.

c
> It highlights to Scrooge and to the reader the Victorians' belief in the importance of family above everything else.

D
> Although this shows the poor in a negative light, it also shows the consequences of the rich ignoring them.

d
> It suggests that, although there was a huge gap between rich and poor in the 1840s, the rich should still treat the poor with respect.

(a) The sentences either comment on the **impact** of the evidence in the paragraph or comment on the novel's **context**. Decide which heading ('Impact' or 'Context') to add 🖉 above each of the columns of text.

(b) Which comments on context are relevant to which comments on impact? Draw 🖉 lines linking them.

(c) Which of the sentences above would you include in a paragraph analysing how Dickens presents the poor at this point in the novel and in what order would you sequence them? Write 🖉 the sentence order here.

☐ ☐ ☐ ☐ ☐ ☐ ☐ ☐

Commenting on context

To comment effectively on context, you need to:

- use a relevant contextual point to develop your analysis of a key point, supported by evidence
- explore what this contextual idea adds to your understanding of Dickens' intention and the reader's response.

Look at this exam-style question you saw at the start of the unit.

Exam-style question

Starting with this extract, how does Dickens present the poor in *A Christmas Carol*?

Write about:

- how Dickens presents the poor in this extract
- how Dickens presents the poor in the novel as a whole.

(1) Now look at a paragraph focusing on the novel as a whole, taken from one student's response to the question.

The most shocking part of the story in which Dickens presents the poor is when the Ghost of Christmas Present shows Scrooge the two children, Ignorance and Want. They are described as 'yellow' and 'wolfish', creating a disturbing impression of the poor. The Ghost makes it clear that Man is responsible, suggesting that the richer people in society have created children like Ignorance and Want by exploiting them, making them work long hours in poor conditions for very little money. Many Victorians blamed the poor for being poor, thinking they were lazy and irresponsible, so this scene highlights Dickens' concern at the way in which the Victorians treated the poor and encourages the reader to recognise their responsibility for them and see the importance of giving to charity.

- uses a key event as evidence
- uses a quotation as evidence
- comments on the impact of the evidence
- identifies a relevant contextual point
- explores Dickens' intention in the light of this contextual point
- explores the reader's response in the light of this contextual point

Can you identify all the different things the student has included in this paragraph? Link 🖉 the annotations to the paragraph to show where the student has included them.

Your turn!

You are now going to **write your own answer** in response to the exam-style question.

Starting with this extract, how does Dickens present the poor in *A Christmas Carol*?

Write about:

• how Dickens presents the poor in this extract

• how Dickens presents the poor in the novel as a whole.

(30 marks)

1 Write ✏ **one** or **two** sentences, summarising your critical judgement in response to the question: how does Dickens present the poor in *A Christmas Carol*?

....

....

2 Which key events in the novel would support your critical judgement? Note ✏ them below.

Evidence

3 Look at all the evidence you have gathered. Think about:

• what your evidence suggests about the poor

• what your evidence suggests about Dickens' intention: how might the reader respond at this point?

Annotate ✏ your evidence with your ideas.

4 Now think about the relevant contextual points you could make in your response. Annotate ✏ your evidence with your ideas.

5 Look at your annotated evidence.

a Which are your strongest ideas? Tick ✓ them.

b Number ✏ the ideas that you have ticked, and sequence them here to build an argument that supports your critical judgement.

6 Now write ✏ your response to the exam-style question above on paper.

Review your skills

Check up

Review your response to the exam-style question on page 63. Tick ✓ the column to show how well you think you have done each of the following.

	Not quite ✓	Nearly there ✓	Got it! ✓
identified relevant contextual points	☐	☐	☐
used relevant contextual points to develop my analysis	☐	☐	☐
explored Dickens' intention and the reader's response in the light of the novel's context	☐	☐	☐

Look over all of your work in this unit. Note 🖉 down the **three** most important things to remember when commenting on context.

1. ....

2. ....

3. ....

Need more practice?

Look at this exam-style question, this time relating to the extract from Chapter 4 on page 77 (Extract E).

Look at this exam-style question, this time relating to the extract from Chapter 4 on page 77 (Extract E).

Exam-style question

Starting with this extract, how does Dickens present Scrooge as a man who is willing to change?

Write about:

- how Dickens presents Scrooge in this extract
- how Dickens presents Scrooge as a man who is willing to change in the novel as a whole.

(30 marks)

Write 🖉 your response to this question.
You'll find some suggested points to refer to in the Answers section.

How confident do you feel about each of these **skills**? Colour 🖉 in the bars.

① How do I know which contextual ideas to write about?

② How do I comment on context?

③ How do I build my comments on context into my analysis?

⑨ Developing a critical writing style

This unit will help you to express your ideas about *A Christmas Carol* as clearly and precisely as possible. The skills you will build are to:

- select vocabulary to express your ideas precisely
- link your ideas to express them clearly
- extend your sentences to develop ideas more fully.

In the exam you will face questions like the one below. This is about the extract on the next page. At the end of the unit you will **write one paragraph** in response to this question.

Exam-style question

Starting with this extract, how does Dickens present Scrooge's transformation in *A Christmas Carol*?

Write about:

- how Dickens presents Scrooge's transformation in this extract
- how Dickens presents Scrooge's transformation in the novel as a whole.

(30 marks)

Before you tackle the question you will work through three key questions in the **skills boosts** to help you develop a critical writing style.

① How do I choose vocabulary that expresses my ideas precisely?

② How can I link my ideas to express them more clearly?

③ How can I extend my sentences to develop my ideas more fully?

Read the extract on the next page from Chapter 5 of *A Christmas Carol*.

As you read, think about the following:

What has happened before this extract? What happens after this extract?	How does Scrooge's behaviour in the extract show he has changed?	How do Scrooge's actions in the extract suggest the reasons for his transformation?

Exam-style question

Read the following extract from Chapter 5 of *A Christmas Carol* and then answer the question on page 65.

At this point in the novel, Scrooge has woken on Christmas morning after being visited by the Spirits overnight.

Extract A | Chapter 5 of *A Christmas Carol* by Charles Dickens

"I don't know what day of the month it is!" said Scrooge. "I don't know how long I've been among the Spirits. I don't know anything. I'm quite a baby. Never mind. I don't care. I'd rather be a baby. Hallo! Whoop! Hallo here!"

He was checked in his transports by the churches ringing out the lustiest peals he had ever heard. Clash, clang, hammer; ding, dong, bell. Bell, dong, ding, hammer, clang, clash! Oh, glorious, glorious!

5   Running to the window, he opened it, and put out his head. No fog, no mist; clear, bright, jovial, stirring, cold; cold, piping for the blood to dance to; Golden sunlight; Heavenly sky; sweet fresh air; merry bells. Oh, glorious. Glorious!

"What's to-day?" cried Scrooge, calling downward to a boy in Sunday clothes, who perhaps had loitered in to look about him.

"EH?" returned the boy, with all his might of wonder.

10   "What's to-day, my fine fellow?" said Scrooge.

"To-day!" replied the boy. "Why, CHRISTMAS DAY."

"It's Christmas Day!" said Scrooge to himself. "I haven't missed it. The Spirits have done it all in one night. They can do anything they like. Of course they can. Of course they can. Hallo, my fine fellow!"

"Hallo!" returned the boy.

15   "Do you know the Poulterer's, in the next street but one, at the corner?" Scrooge inquired.

"I should hope I did," replied the lad.

"An intelligent boy!" said Scrooge. "A remarkable boy! Do you know whether they've sold the prize Turkey that was hanging up there? Not the little prize Turkey: the big one?"

"What, the one as big as me?" returned the boy.

20   "What a delightful boy!" said Scrooge. "It's a pleasure to talk to him. Yes, my buck!"

"It's hanging there now," replied the boy.

"Is it?" said Scrooge. "Go and buy it."

"Walk-ER!" exclaimed the boy.

"No, no," said Scrooge, "I am in earnest. Go and buy it, and tell 'em to bring it here, that I may give them the
25   direction where to take it. Come back with the man, and I'll give you a shilling. Come back with him in less than five minutes, and I'll give you half-a-crown!"

The boy was off like a shot. He must have had a steady hand at a trigger who could have got a shot off half so fast.

"I'll send it to Bob Cratchit's!" whispered Scrooge, rubbing his hands, and splitting with a laugh. "He sha'n't know who sends it. It's twice the size of Tiny Tim. Joe Miller never made such a joke as sending it to Bob's will be!"

30   The hand in which he wrote the address was not a steady one, but write it he did, somehow, and went down stairs to open the street door, ready for the coming of the poulterer's man.

1 How do I choose vocabulary that expresses my ideas precisely?

You need to choose precise vocabulary to describe your response to the novel as fully and accurately as possible.

① How would you describe Dickens' presentation of Scrooge at **each** of these points in the novel?

Scrooge...

Chapter 1	A rejects his nephew and a man collecting for the poor	
Chapter 2	B sobs at the sight of his childhood self alone	
	C watches a vision of Christmas at Fezziwig's	
Chapter 3	D sees the Cratchits enjoying Christmas	
	E sees his nephew enjoying Christmas	
	F sees Ignorance and Want	
Chapter 4	G sees people selling a dead man's belongings	
	H sees his own gravestone	
Chapter 5	I wakes on Christmas morning	
	J buys a turkey for the Cratchits	

Choose **two** words from the list below and write 🖉 them next to the relevant point in the novel. Aim to choose words that describe your response as precisely as possible. You could choose two words with a similar meaning, or two very different words expressing different possible responses.

cold-hearted	pathetic	happy	sympathetic	kind	repentant
isolated	vulnerable	joyful	understanding	generous	relieved
unkind	distraught	ecstatic	sensitive	thoughtful	regretful
cruel	anxious	excitable	affectionate	considerate	grateful
mean	unhappy	hysterical	caring	compassionate	apologetic

② Now think about Dickens' intention: how did he want the readers to respond to Scrooge at these points in the novel? Choose **one** or **two** of the words below and add 🖉 them to each of the key points in question ①.

excitement	disappointment	tension	fear	admiration
happiness	relief	disgust	shock	sorrow
laughter	concern	anger	surprise	sympathy

2 How can I link my ideas to express them more clearly?

You can use conjunctions to link your ideas, helping you to express your ideas more clearly and fluently.

Coordinating conjunctions link related or contrasting ideas:	**Subordinating conjunctions** express more complex connections:
and but or so	• an explanation, e.g. because in order to
	• a comparison, e.g. although whereas
	• a sequence, e.g. when after until

① Look at these pairs of sentences.

A

☐ The Ghost shows Scrooge his gravestone. He promises to change his ways.

☐ Scrooge claims to hate Christmas. He clearly enjoys the vision of Christmas Past at Fezziwig's.

☐ Scrooge is transformed. He recognises the importance of Christmas.

B

☐ When the Ghost shows Scrooge his gravestone, he promises to change his ways.

☐ Although Scrooge claims to hate Christmas, he clearly enjoys the vision of Christmas Past at Fezziwig's.

☐ Scrooge is transformed because he recognises the importance of Christmas.

a Circle Ⓐ the **conjunctions** in the sentences labelled B.

b Tick ✓ the version of each sentence that you feel is most clearly and fluently expressed.

② Rewrite ✏ these pairs of sentences, using a conjunction to link them. Remember to choose and position your conjunction carefully to express each idea as clearly and fluently as possible.

Scrooge sees the Cratchits enjoying Christmas.	**+**	He asks if Tiny Tim will live.

....

Scrooge hates Christmas.	**+**	He thinks it is a waste of money.

....

Scrooge gradually realises he wants to change.	**+**	He only really changes at the end of the novel.

....

3 How can I extend my sentences to develop my ideas more fully?

One way to extend your sentences, and develop your ideas, is by using conjunctions. Other ways include:
- using present participles: a verb ending in –ing
- using the pronoun which.

Conjunctions						
	and	but	when	as	before	after
	although	if	whereas	unless	because	since

You could complete this sentence:

> Scrooge is faced with the disturbing sight of Ignorance and Want...

- using this conjunction: → after he has seen the joy of Christmas at his nephew's.

- or a present participle: → making him ask, '"Have they no refuge or resource?"'

- or which: → which shows that he can feel sympathy and compassion.

(1) Complete ✏ this sentence in **three** different ways.

> The Ghost of Christmas Yet To Come shows Scrooge his own gravestone...

a Use a conjunction: ....

b Use a present participle: ....

c Use which: ....

You can use which or a present participle to avoid repeatedly beginning sentences with 'This suggests...' or 'This shows...'.

For example:

Scrooge makes a large donation to charity. This suggests how much he has changed.	Scrooge makes a large donation to charity, which suggests how much he has changed.	Scrooge makes a large donation to charity, suggesting how much he has changed.

(2) Change ✏ these sentences to make them a single sentence, using a present participle or which.

> Scrooge refuses to spend Christmas with his nephew. This creates the impression that he sees no value in family life.

> Scrooge becomes 'a second father' to Tiny Tim. This shows that he has finally recognised the importance of family life.

Unit 9 Developing a critical writing style   **69**

Developing a critical writing style

To express your ideas clearly and precisely, you can:

- select vocabulary that expresses your ideas precisely
- link your ideas using conjunctions, present participles, etc. to develop and express them clearly.

Now look at this exam-style question you saw on page 65.

Exam-style question

Starting with this extract, how does Dickens present Scrooge's transformation in *A Christmas Carol*?

Write about:

- how Dickens presents Scrooge's transformation in this extract
- how Dickens present Scrooge's transformation in the novel as a whole.

(1) Look at a short paragraph from one student's response to the question.

At the start of the novel Scrooge is presented as mean and nasty. He won't go to his nephew's for Christmas. He says it is a waste of money. He will not give money to charity. He says he cannot afford it. This suggests that it is money that is Scrooge's life. It gives the impression that Christmas and family are nothing to him.

a Underline (A) **at least three** examples of vocabulary that could be more precise.

b Note (✏) down in the margin **at least two** alternative vocabulary choices for each one.

c Highlight (✏) any of the sentences that you feel should be linked or developed to improve the clarity and precision of the writing.

d Write (✏) an improved version of this paragraph, either by adjusting the text above or by rewriting it in the space below.

....

....

....

....

....

....

Your turn!

You are now going to **write one paragraph** in response to the exam-style question.

Starting with this extract, how does Dickens present Scrooge's transformation in *A Christmas Carol*?

Write about:

- how Dickens presents Scrooge's transformation in this extract
- how Dickens presents Scrooge's transformation in the novel as a whole.

(30 marks)

1 **a** Think about some of the key events in the novel. Do they show Scrooge unchanged, changing, or changed? ✓

Scrooge...	Unchanged	Changing	Changed
• refuses his nephew's Christmas invitation	☐	☐	☐
• sobs at the sight of his childhood self	☐	☐	☐
• enjoys Fezziwig's Christmas celebration	☐	☐	☐
• enjoys the Cratchits' Christmas celebration	☐	☐	☐
• enjoys his nephew's Christmas celebration	☐	☐	☐
• sees Ignorance and Want	☐	☐	☐
• sees people talking about a dead man's belongings	☐	☐	☐
• sees his own gravestone	☐	☐	☐
• buys a turkey and goes to his nephew's	☐	☐	☐

b Choose **one** or **two** of the key events from the novel which you can explore in your response to the exam-style question. You could choose from the list above, or use your own ideas. Note 🖉 them on paper.

c Look at each of your chosen events: how is Scrooge presented? How and why is Scrooge changing? How has Dickens created that impression? Add 🖉 your ideas to your notes.

d Use your ideas to write 🖉 a paragraph on paper in response to the exam-style question.

> **Hint:** Remember to:
> - choose your vocabulary carefully
> - think about ways in which you can link your ideas to develop and express them clearly and precisely.

Review your skills

Check up

Review your response to the exam-style question on page 71. Tick ⊘ the column to show how well you think you have done each of the following.

	Not quite ⊘	Nearly there ⊘	Got it! ⊘
selected precise vocabulary	☐	☐	☐
linked and developed my ideas clearly and precisely using conjunctions, present participles, etc.	☐	☐	☐

Look over all of your work in this unit. Note 🖉 down the **three** most important things to remember when trying to express your ideas as clearly and precisely as possible.

1. ....

2. ....

3. ....

Need more practice?

You can EITHER:

① Look again at your paragraph written in response to the exam-style question on page 71. Rewrite 🖉 it, experimenting with different vocabulary choices and sentence structures, linking your ideas in different ways. Which are most effective in expressing your ideas clearly and precisely?

AND/OR:

② Choose a **second** point from the suggestions on page 71. Write 🖉 a further paragraph in response to the exam-style question, focusing closely on your vocabulary choice and sentence structures.

How confident do you feel about each of these **skills?** Colour 🖉 in the bars.

① How do I choose vocabulary that expresses my ideas precisely?

② How can I link my ideas to express them more clearly?

③ How can I extend my sentences to develop my ideas more fully?

More practice questions

Units 1 and 2

Exam-style question

Read the following extract from Chapter 1 of *A Christmas Carol* and then answer the question that follows.

In this extract Scrooge is explaining to the Ghost of Jacob Marley that indigestion often makes him imagine supernatural beings.

Extract A | Chapter 1 of *A Christmas Carol* by Charles Dickens

"You see this toothpick?" said Scrooge, returning quickly to the charge, for the reason just assigned; and wishing, though it were only for a second, to divert the vision's stony gaze from himself.

"I do," replied the Ghost.

"You are not looking at it," said Scrooge.

5   "But I see it," said the Ghost, "notwithstanding."

"Well!" returned Scrooge, "I have but to swallow this, and be for the rest of my days persecuted by a legion of goblins, all of my own creation. Humbug, I tell you – humbug!"

At this, the spirit raised a frightful cry, and shook its chain with such a dismal and appalling noise, that Scrooge held on tight to his chair, to save himself from falling in a swoon. But how much greater was his

10   horror, when the phantom taking off the bandage round its head, as if it were too warm to wear in-doors, its lower jaw dropped down upon its breast!

Scrooge fell upon his knees, and clasped his hands before his face.

"Mercy!" he said. "Dreadful apparition, why do you trouble me?"

"Man of the worldly mind!" replied the Ghost, "do you believe in me or not?"

15   "I do," said Scrooge. "I must. But why do spirits walk the earth, and why do they come to me?"

"It is required of every man," the Ghost returned, "that the spirit within him should walk abroad among his fellow-men, and travel far and wide; and if that spirit goes not forth in life, it is condemned to do so after death. It is doomed to wander through the world – oh, woe is me! – and witness what it cannot share, but might have shared on earth, and turned to happiness!"

20   Again the spectre raised a cry, and shook its chain, and wrung its shadowy hands.

"You are fettered," said Scrooge, trembling. "Tell me why?"

"I wear the chain I forged in life," replied the Ghost. "I made it link by link, and yard by yard; I girded it on of my own free will, and of my own free will I wore it. Is its pattern strange to *you*?"

Scrooge trembled more and more.

25   "Or would you know," pursued the Ghost, "the weight and length of the strong coil you bear yourself? It was full as heavy and as long as this, seven Christmas Eves ago. You have laboured on it, since. It is a ponderous chain!"

Scrooge glanced about him on the floor, in the expectation of finding himself surrounded by some fifty or sixty fathoms of iron cable: but he could see nothing.

"Jacob," he said, imploringly. "Old Jacob Marley, tell me more. Speak comfort to me, Jacob."

30   "I have none to give," the Ghost replied.

Starting with this extract, how does Dickens present the supernatural in *A Christmas Carol*?

Write about:

• how Dickens presents the supernatural in this extract

• how Dickens presents the supernatural in the novel as a whole.

(30 marks)

Unit 1 Which key events in the novel would you choose to write ✏ about in your response to this question?

Unit 2 Write ✏ **one** or **two** paragraphs in response to this question, focusing on the extract only.

Units 3 and 4

Read the following extract from Chapter 2 of *A Christmas Carol* and then answer the question that follows.

In this extract the Ghost of Christmas Past shows Scrooge a scene from his past in which his fiancée, Belle, breaks off their engagement.

Extract A | Chapter 2 of *A Christmas Carol* by Charles Dickens

"My time grows short," observed the Spirit. "Quick!"

This was not addressed to Scrooge, or to anyone whom he could see, but it produced an immediate effect. For again Scrooge saw himself. He was older now; a man in the prime of life. His face had not the harsh and rigid lines of later years; but it had begun to wear the signs of care and avarice. There was an eager, greedy,
5   restless motion in the eye, which showed the passion that had taken root, and where the shadow of the growing tree would fall.

He was not alone, but sat by the side of a fair young girl in a mourning-dress: in whose eyes there were tears, which sparkled in the light that shone out of the Ghost of Christmas Past.

"It matters little," she said, softly. "To you, very little. Another idol has displaced me: and if it can cheer and
10   comfort you in time to come, as I would have tried to do, I have no just cause to grieve."

"What Idol has displaced you?" he rejoined.

"A golden one."

"This is the even-handed dealing of the world!" he said. "There is nothing on which it is so hard as poverty; and there is nothing it professes to condemn with such severity as the pursuit of wealth!"

15   "You fear the world too much," she answered, gently. "All your other hopes have merged into the hope of being beyond the chance of its sordid reproach. I have seen your nobler aspirations fall off one by one, until the master-passion, Gain, engrosses you. Have I not?"

"What then?" he retorted. "Even if I have grown so much wiser, what then? I am not changed towards you."

She shook her head.

20   "Am I?"

"Our contract is an old one. It was made when we were both poor and content to be so, until, in good season, we could improve our worldly fortune by our patient industry. You *are* changed. When it was made, you were another man."

"I was a boy," he said impatiently.

25   "Your own feeling tells you that you were not what you are," she returned. "I am. That which promised happiness when we were one in heart, is fraught with misery now that we are two. How often and how keenly I have thought of this, I will not say. It is enough that I have thought of it, and can release you."

Starting with this extract, explore how Dickens presents money in *A Christmas Carol*.

Write about:

- how Dickens presents money in this extract
- how Dickens presents money in the novel as a whole.

(30 marks)

Unit 3 Write 🖉 **one** or **two** paragraphs in response to this question, focusing on the extract only.

Unit 4 Write 🖉 **two** paragraphs in response to this question, focusing on the second bullet point: the novel as a whole.

Exam-style question

Read the following extract from Chapter 3 of A *Christmas Carol* and then answer the question that follows.

In this extract the Ghost of Christmas Present shows Scrooge a vision of the streets of London on Christmas morning.

Extract A | Chapter 3 of A *Christmas Carol* by Charles Dickens

The Grocers'! oh, the Grocers'! nearly closed, with perhaps two shutters down, or one; but through those gaps such glimpses! It was not alone that the scales descending on the counter made a merry sound, or that the twine and roller parted company so briskly, or that the canisters were rattling up and down like juggling tricks, or even that the blended scents of tea and coffee were so grateful to the nose, or even that the raisins
5   were so plentiful and rare, the almonds so extremely white, the sticks of cinnamon so long and straight, the other spices so delicious, the candied fruits so caked and spotted with molten sugar as to make the coldest lookers-on feel faint and subsequently bilious. Nor was it that the figs were moist and pulpy, or that the French plums blushed in modest tartness from their highly-decorated boxes, or that everything was good to eat and in its Christmas dress; but the customers were all so hurried and so eager in the hopeful promise of
10   the day, that they tumbled up against each other at the door, crashing their wicker baskets wildly, and left their purchases upon the counter, and came running back to fetch them, and committed hundreds of the like mistakes, in the best humour possible; while the Grocer and his people were so frank and fresh that the polished hearts with which they fastened their aprons behind might have been their own, worn outside for general inspection, and for Christmas daws to peck at if they chose.
15   But soon the steeples called good people all, to church and chapel, and away they came, flocking through the streets in their best clothes, and with their gayest faces. And at the same time there emerged, from scores of bye streets, lanes, and nameless turnings, innumerable people, carrying their dinners to the bakers' shops. The sight of these poor revellers appeared to interest the Spirit very much, for he stood with Scrooge beside him in a baker's doorway, and taking off the covers as their bearers passed, sprinkled incense on their dinners
20   from his torch. And it was a very uncommon kind of torch, for once or twice when there were angry words between some dinner-carriers who had jostled with each other, he shed a few drops of water on them from it, and their good humour was restored directly. For they said, it was a shame to quarrel upon Christmas Day. And so it was! God love it, so it was!

Starting with this extract, how does Dickens present the people of Victorian Britain in A *Christmas Carol*?

Write about:
- how Dickens presents Victorian Britain in this extract
- how Dickens presents Victorian Britain in the novel as a whole.

(30 marks)

(**Unit 5**) Plan ✐ your response to this question.

(**Unit 6**) Write ✐ your response to this question.

Read the following extract from Chapter 4 of *A Christmas Carol* and then answer the question that follows.

In this extract Scrooge watches as a group of poor people sell a dead man's belongings to Joe, a shopkeeper.

Extract A | Chapter 4 of *A Christmas Carol* by Charles Dickens

"I hope he didn't die of anything catching? Eh?" said old Joe, stopping in his work, and looking up.

"Don't you be afraid of that," returned the woman. "I an't so fond of his company that I'd loiter about him for such things, if he did. Ah! you may look through that shirt till your eyes ache; but you won't find a hole in it, nor a threadbare place. It's the best he had, and a fine one too. They'd have wasted it, if it hadn't been for me."

5 "What do you call wasting of it?" asked old Joe.

"Putting it on him to be buried in, to be sure," replied the woman with a laugh. "Somebody was fool enough to do it, but I took it off again. If calico an't good enough for such a purpose, it isn't good enough for anything. It's quite as becoming to the body. He can't look uglier than he did in that one."

Scrooge listened to this dialogue in horror. As they sat grouped about their spoil, in the scanty light afforded
10 by the old man's lamp, he viewed them with a detestation and disgust, which could hardly have been greater, though they had been obscene demons, marketing the corpse itself.

"Ha, ha!" laughed the same woman, when old Joe, producing a flannel bag with money in it, told out their several gains upon the ground. "This is the end of it, you see! He frightened every one away from him when he was alive, to profit us when he was dead! Ha, ha, ha!"

15 "Spirit!" said Scrooge, shuddering from head to foot. "I see, I see. The case of this unhappy man might be my own. My life tends that way, now. Merciful Heaven, what is this!"

He recoiled in terror, for the scene had changed, and now he almost touched a bed: a bare, uncurtained bed; on which, beneath a ragged sheet, there lay a something covered up, which, though it was dumb, announced itself in awful language.

20 The room was very dark, too dark to be observed with any accuracy, though Scrooge glanced round it in obedience to a secret impulse, anxious to know what kind of room it was. A pale light, rising in the outer air, fell straight upon the bed; and on it, plundered and bereft, unwatched, unwept, uncared for, was the body of this man.

Starting with this extract, how does Dickens present choices and consequences in *A Christmas Carol*?

Write about:

- how Dickens presents choices and consequences in this extract
- how Dickens presents choices and consequences in the novel as a whole.

(30 marks)

Unit 7 Plan ✎ your response to the question.

Read the following extract from Chapter 4 of *A Christmas Carol* and then answer the question that follows.

In this extract the Ghost of Christmas Yet To Come shows Scrooge a gravestone.

Extract A | Chapter 4 of *A Christmas Carol* by Charles Dickens

"This court," said Scrooge, "through which we hurry now, is where my place of occupation is, and has been for a length of time. I see the house. Let me behold what I shall be, in days to come!"

The Spirit stopped; the hand was pointed elsewhere.

"The house is yonder," Scrooge exclaimed. "Why do you point away?"

5 The inexorable finger underwent no change.

Scrooge hastened to the window of his office, and looked in. It was an office still, but not his. The furniture was not the same, and the figure in the chair was not himself. The Phantom pointed as before.

He joined it once again, and wondering why and whither he had gone, accompanied it until they reached an iron gate. He paused to look round before entering.

10 A churchyard. Here, then, the wretched man whose name he had now to learn, lay underneath the ground. It was a worthy place. Walled in by houses; overrun by grass and weeds, the growth of vegetation's death, not life; choked up with too much burying; fat with repleted appetite. A worthy place!

The Spirit stood among the graves, and pointed down to One. He advanced towards it trembling. The Phantom was exactly as it had been, but he dreaded that he saw new meaning in its solemn shape.

15 "Before I draw nearer to that stone to which you point," said Scrooge, "answer me one question. Are these the shadows of the things that Will be, or are they shadows of the things that May be, only?"

Still the Ghost pointed downward to the grave by which it stood.

"Men's courses will foreshadow certain ends, to which, if persevered in, they must lead," said Scrooge. "But if the courses be departed from, the ends will change. Say it is thus with what you show me!"

20 The Spirit was immovable as ever.

Scrooge crept towards it, trembling as he went; and following the finger, read upon the stone of the neglected grave his own name, EBENEZER SCROOGE.

"Am I that man who lay upon the bed?" he cried, upon his knees.

The finger pointed from the grave to him, and back again.

25 "No, Spirit! Oh no, no!"

The finger still was there.

"Spirit!" he cried, tight clutching at its robe, "hear me! I am not the man I was. I will not be the man I must have been but for this intercourse. Why show me this, if I am past all hope!"

For the first time the hand appeared to shake.

30 "Good Spirit," he pursued, as down upon the ground he fell before it: "Your nature intercedes for me, and pities me. Assure me that I yet may change these shadows you have shown me, by an altered life!"

The kind hand trembled.

"I will honour Christmas in my heart, and try to keep it all the year. I will live in the Past, the Present, and the Future. The Spirits of all Three shall strive within me. I will not shut out the lessons that they teach. Oh, tell
35 me I may sponge away the writing on this stone!"

Starting with this extract, how does Dickens present Scrooge as a man who is willing to change?

Write about:

• how Dickens presents Scrooge in this extract

• how Dickens presents Scrooge as a man who is willing to change in the novel as a whole.

(30 marks)

Unit 8 Write ✎ your response to this question.

Answers

Unit 1

Page 3

1. a. 4: the Ghosts of Jacob Marley, Christmas Past, Christmas Present, Christmas Yet To Come

   b. See diagram below.

2. a/b See diagram below.

3. a

Past: Fan, Belle, Fezziwig

Present: Fred, The Cratchits, the Ghost of Jacob Marley, the Ghost of Christmas Past, the Ghost of Christmas Present, the Ghost of Christmas Yet To Come, Ignorance and Want

Future: Fred, The Cratchits, a group of businessmen, a group of poor people

1. b, 2. a/b, 3. b For example:

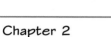

> **Chapter 1**
> Scrooge is mean to **Bob Cratchit** and **Fred**.
> He is visited by the Ghost of **Jacob Marley**.

⬇

> **Chapter 2**
> **The Ghost of Christmas Past** shows Scrooge scenes from his past featuring **Fan**, **Fezziwig** and **Belle**.

⬇

> **Chapter 3**
> **The Ghost of Christmas Present** shows Scrooge Christmas at the **Cratchits'**, at **Fred's**, and shows him **Ignorance and Want**.

⬇

> **Chapter 4**
> **The Ghost of Christmas Yet To Come** shows Scrooge **groups of businessmen and poor people** talking about his death, and the **Cratchits** after **Tiny Tim's** death.

⬇

> **Chapter 5**
> Scrooge buys the **Cratchits** a turkey and spends Christmas at **Fred's** house.

Page 4

1. a. All the events in Chapters 1 and 5.

   b. All the events in Chapters 2, 3 and 4, although arguably the events of Chapter 2 do not show so explicitly why Scrooge decides to change.

   c. For example: The events of Chapter 2 develop the character of Scrooge, showing him and the reader what he has lost through his greed and heartlessness, and so creating some sympathy in the reader.

Page 5

1. b Possible answers include:

   - Scrooge is mean to his employee, Bob Cratchit: this clearly establishes the character of Scrooge and, contrasted with his behaviour in Chapter 5, shows how much he has changed by the end of the novel.

   - The Ghost shows him Christmas at the Cratchits' house: this shows the power of Christmas, and the power of the family, to overcome poverty.

   - The Ghost shows him Christmas at his nephew's house: this shows the joy of Christmas and the importance of family.

   - The Ghost shows Scrooge his gravestone: this has a significant impact on Scrooge and his decision to change his ways.

   - Scrooge buys the Cratchit family a turkey: the gift, and the people he buys it for, show how much Scrooge's attitude has changed since Chapter 1.

Page 6

1.

<u>Before this extract:</u> We meet Scrooge for the first time. He is described as 'cold' and 'tight-fisted'. <u>After this extract:</u> Scrooge refuses to give money to charity.	Shows awareness of **where** in the novel the extract is taken from.
So in Chapter 1, Scrooge shown as stubborn and heartless to everyone – interested in no one but himself and nothing but his money.	Makes a clear, direct **response** to the question.
stubborn and heartless	Uses **key words** from the question.
e.g. Contrast of Fred and Scrooge	Makes a **range of points**.
e.g. 'a cheerful voice' / 'Bah!'	Supports points with **evidence**.
e.g. emphasises difference/ heartlessness	**Comments** on the significance of the writer's choices.

Page 7

1. a. All events in Chapter 1.

   b. All events in Chapter 5; other key events that have a significant impact on Scrooge's transformation, for example:

   - The Ghost shows him Christmas at the Cratchits' house.

   - The Ghost shows him the Cratchits' home; Tiny Tim has died.

   c. Answers will vary.

Page 8

Responses could focus on:

- the presentation of the Ghost of Jacob Marley

- the presentation of the Ghosts of Christmas Past, Present and Yet To Come
- the significance of what each ghost reveals to Scrooge.

Unit 2

Page 11

1 **a** 1 (A), 2 (B), 3 (C)

b For example:

A: Section 1 presents Bob Cratchit as a man who takes great joy in life and time with his family, despite his poverty. This is in strong contrast to Scrooge, emphasising his solitary, self-contained life.

B: Section 2 presents Scrooge as living a solitary, miserable life with little interest in anything but his money.

C: In Section 3 the description of Scrooge's chambers reflects his character: cold, isolated and gloomy.

Page 12

1 **a** Scrooge's home is 'gloomy', 'dreary' and 'dark'.

b Scrooge is a friendless miser so it is not surprising he lives alone in an unappealing building.

c/d It reflects, and adds to the reader's impression of, his character. The building is isolated, 'up a yard, where it had so little business to be', and cold, 'The fog and frost ... hung about the black old gateway of the house'.

2 For example: He eats his 'melancholy dinner in his usual melancholy tavern' alone, suggesting his solitary self-containment. He spends the rest of the evening 'with his banker's-book', suggesting he is interested only in himself and his money.

Page 13

1 All are valid.

2 For example: D, C, E, B, F, A or A, B, F, C, E, D

3 For example:

[A] The description of Scrooge's home powerfully develops the reader's impression that he lives a self-contained and solitary life.

For example, [B] his home is 'a gloomy suite of rooms' which are 'up a yard'.

This suggests that [F] the building is set apart and isolated from all the other nearby houses, reflecting Scrooge's gloomy, solitary nature.

Similarly, [C] Dickens describes how 'the fog and frost ... hung about the black old gateway'.

It implies that [E] the gateway, which should be a welcoming entrance to his home, is frozen and forbidding.

In this way, [D] Dickens presents Scrooge's home to reflect his character because, like him, it is cold, unwelcoming and set apart from the rest of society.

4 Key point: A

Evidence: B, C

Comment: E, F

Response: D

Page 14

1 **a** The student has achieved all of the criteria.

b B Key point: *In this extract, Scrooge is clearly shown to lead a self-contained and solitary life.*

C Evidence: *The reader is told that, after leaving his office, he eats his 'melancholy dinner in his usual melancholy tavern',* ...

D Comment: *... which suggests that everything he does and everywhere he goes is 'melancholy'.*

C Evidence: *He spends 'the rest of the evening with his banker's-book',* ...

D Comment: *... which implies that, instead of spending the evening in a tavern with a friend or with family, he would rather spend it with his money.*

E Response: *The impression created in this sentence is of an isolated, solitary man who is interested only in business and profit.*

Page 16

Responses could focus on:

- Scrooge's initial cynicism: ' "Humbug, I tell you – humbug!" '
- the supernatural as disturbing and terrifying: 'its lower jaw dropped down'
- Scrooge's terror: ' "Mercy!" '
- Dickens' use of the ghosts to show Scrooge the consequences of his choices: ' "It is a ponderous chain!" '

Unit 3

Page 19

1 **a** ' "Good Heaven!" he said'; 'clasping his hands together,'

b ' "Good Heaven!" '; 'clasping'

c ' "Good Heaven!" ' suggests surprise or amazement; 'clasping' suggests a powerful reaction of excitement or anxiety.

2 A:

a Scrooge is upset but is reluctant to admit it.

b/c 'trembling' and 'catching' suggest upset; 'muttering' and 'pimple' suggest his reluctance to admit it.

B:

a Scrooge's childhood was lonely and miserable; he is deeply upset by the thought of it.

b/c 'solitary' and 'neglected' suggest a lonely, miserable childhood; 'sobbed' highlights his upset. This emotional response suggests a softening of his hard-hearted nature.

Page 20

1 All combinations are valid. The section shows Scrooge's confusion but determination in his denial of the joy he feels; his shock and anguish as he sobs. It arguably suggests the Ghost's determination to show Scrooge scenes that will eventually change him.

2 **a** For example:

A: 'Why was he filled with gladness when he heard them give each other Merry Christmas, as they parted at cross-roads and bye-ways, for their several homes?'

B: 'And he sobbed.'

C: 'What was merry Christmas to Scrooge?'

D: '"Out upon merry Christmas!"'

b For example:

In sentence A, Dickens suggests that Scrooge cannot understand the feelings of gladness he is experiencing.

In sentence B, Dickens suggests that Scrooge is deeply moved by memories of his neglected childhood.

In sentence C, Dickens suggests that Scrooge is confused about his feelings towards Christmas.

In sentence D, Dickens suggests that Scrooge is determined to maintain his dislike of Christmas.

c For example:

In sentence B, Dickens uses a short sentence to give dramatic emphasis to Scrooge's anguish.

In sentence C, Dickens uses a rhetorical question to highlight Scrooge's confusion at the emotions he is feeling.

In sentence D, Dickens uses an exclamation to emphasise Scrooge's determination to dislike Christmas.

Page 21

1 All comments are valid.

2 Comments are likely to focus on how:

- the Ghost's description of the young Scrooge as 'solitary' and 'neglected' creates sympathy for Scrooge
- the verb 'sobbed' highlights the impact of this scene on Scrooge
- the use of two short sentences adds dramatic emphasis to Scrooge's reaction.

Page 22

key point focusing on the key words in the question	When Scrooge recognises the place that the Ghost has brought him to see, Dickens clearly shows it has a significant effect on him:
evidence from the text to support the point	'"Good Heaven!" said Scrooge, clasping his hands together'. ... Scrooge then goes on to explain '"I was bred in this place. I was a boy here."'
comments on the evidence and its impact	The short exclamation at the beginning of this sentence emphasises his surprise, while the verb 'clasping' could suggest powerful feelings of happiness or anxiety. ... Dickens uses short sentences here to suggest how quickly Scrooge is speaking, suggesting his surprise and excitement at seeing it again.
a response to the question	Scrooge's reaction at the start of the extract shows the impact these scenes from his childhood are having on him, encouraging the reader to think that his uncharacteristically enthusiastic and positive reaction may show he is starting to change.

a comment on language choice(s)	the verb 'clasping' could suggest powerful feelings of happiness or anxiety
a comment on choice(s) of structure or sentence form	The short exclamation at the beginning of this sentence emphasises his surprise ... Dickens uses short sentences here to suggest how quickly Scrooge is speaking, suggesting his surprise and excitement at seeing it again.

Page 24

Responses could focus on:

- Scrooge's love of money described as 'the passion that had taken root' and 'the master-passion'
- Money described as his 'idol', implying worship
- Scrooge's fear of poverty
- the consequence of losing his fiancée because of his love of money.

Unit 4

Page 27

1 For example: mean, cruel, heartless, isolated, selfish, bitter

2 For example: generous, kind, charitable, sympathetic, loving

3 All responses are arguable. Although the sight of his own grave ultimately prompts Scrooge's redemption, each key event in the novel shows a step towards it.

Page 28

1 For example:

transformation: Chapter 5: Scrooge celebrates Christmas.

money: Chapter 1: Scrooge will not give money to charity.

family: Chapter 3: The Cratchit family's Christmas celebrations.

Christmas: Chapter 3: the Ghost of Christmas Present shows Scrooge a vision of the poor happily enjoying Christmas morning in the streets of London.

2 Both positive and negative: less important than happiness and family, but corrupting and deadly. Arguably, poverty is presented as unavoidable: there is no suggested solution to the issue, only that the wealthy should support the poor through charity.

3 **a** For example: Fezziwig's party; Christmas at the Cratchit family's house; Christmas at Fred's house.

b For example: A time of plenty, friendship, love and happiness for rich and poor alike.

Page 29

1 **a** C–G

b A–E; D–F

c The few details of Scrooge's earlier life suggest an isolated childhood and a difficult family life dominated by a hard-hearted father. This could, arguably, be the cause of Scrooge's hard-hearted, isolated nature in later life.

(2) (a) All are arguable.

(b) For example: Money dominates and destroys Scrooge's happiness, while the lack of money does not necessarily lead to unhappiness; however, a little generosity can bring great happiness, and the charity of the wealthy can alleviate suffering and bring comfort to the poor.

Page 30

(1) (a) Chapter 1: Scrooge refuses Fred's invitation.

Chapter 3: visions of the streets of London, of the Cratchits' house and Fred's house.

(b) Paragraph 1: ... *contrasting Scrooge's "Bah! Humbug!" attitude to Christmas with that of his nephew, Fred, who thinks Christmas is a time for celebration and happiness.*

Paragraph 2: ... showing that happiness at Christmas is not expensive, even for the richer people of society. Dickens presents this very positive image of Christmas throughout the novel...

(c) *This contrast shows how miserable and hard-hearted Scrooge is because he will not change his ways even for Christmas. It shows he is the exact opposite of Christmas. He is mean, miserable and isolated, whereas Christmas is a time for generosity, happiness and family.*

Page 32

Responses could focus on:

- lack of money as a cause of suffering: for example, the death of Tiny Tim; Ignorance and Want

- the unimportance of money in creating happiness: for example, the few pounds that Fezziwig spent on his Christmas party; the Christmas enjoyed by the Cratchits

- the importance of charity, using money to benefit others: for example, Scrooge's satisfaction and happiness in helping the Cratchits and in donating to charity in Chapter 5.

Unit 5

Page 35

(1) (a) Bob Cratchit is upset that his daughter is not coming home for Christmas: '"Not coming!" said Bob, with a sudden declension in his high spirits'; is a loving, playful father: 'he had been Tim's blood horse all the way from church'; recognises the importance of family at this time of year: '"Not coming upon Christmas Day!"'

(b) For example: A family who are loving and affectionate, seeing Christmas as an opportunity to be together, suggesting the importance of family, especially at Christmas time.

(2) (a/b) All are arguably valid.

(c) For example: Time spent with family at Christmas is a positive, enriching experience.

Page 36

(1) (a) All are arguably valid. However, it could be argued in response to B that charity and generosity are of equal or greater importance.

(b) For example:

Chapter 1a: C, D

Chapter 2a: D

Chapter 2b: A

Chapter 2c: C

Chapter 3a: A, B

Chapter 3b: A, B

Chapter 4a: A, C, E

Chapter 5a: E

Chapter 5b: A, B, E

(2) Key points are likely to focus on the redemption of Scrooge as he recognises the importance of family, which the visions he has been shown repeatedly highlight.

Page 37

(1) A, B, C, D

(2) (a) For example: B, A, C, D, focusing first on Fezziwig, then on Scrooge.

(b) For example: A, C, B, D, focusing first on the negative presentation of Scrooge when he does not recognise the importance of family, then on the positive presentation of characters who do.

Page 38

(1) (a) For example: Characters who do not recognise the importance of family are unhappy; family is a source of happiness.

(b) • *In Chapter 2, Scrooge sobs at the sight of his younger self left at school*

• *Scrooge refuses to go to his nephew's house for Christmas*

• *the Ghost of Christmas Yet To Come shows Scrooge his own death*

• *Scrooge decides he will celebrate Christmas with his nephew*

(c) B

Page 40

Responses could focus on:

In the extract:

- the impression of plentiful and luxurious food: 'raisins ... almonds ... cinnamon ...'

- the impression of excitement at Christmas: 'so hurried and so eager in the hopeful promise of the day'

- the role of the church, which people attend 'in their best clothes, and with their gayest faces'

- 'at the same time' the poor taking 'their dinners to the bakers' shops', implying that church was mainly attended by the wealthier members of society, and suggesting a significant difference in the lives of rich and poor.

In the novel as a whole:

- the differences between rich and poor: for example, in Chapter 5, the businessmen compared with the poor people who steal and sell Scrooge's belongings

- the importance of Christmas to all (except Scrooge)

- the importance of family: for example, the Cratchits

- the reliance of the poor on charity, and the duty of the rich to support them.

Unit 6

Page 43

1. Scrooge, Fred; Christmas, family, generosity
2. a / b A: Scrooge, Ghosts of Christmas; the supernatural

   B: Christmas, poverty

   C: Bob Cratchit; Christmas, poverty, family, generosity

   D: Christmas, poverty

   c B and C are arguably the most significant.
3. a All are valid, however A and D are also relevant to key themes: A shows the significance of Christmas as symbolic of the kindness and generosity that Dickens suggests should be demonstrated throughout the year; D shows that kindness and a recognition of the importance of family are equally significant in the redemption of Scrooge.

   b For example: 'keep it all the year'; 'a second father'.

Page 44

1. For example: Fred is prepared to forgive his Uncle Scrooge for his hard-heartedness.

   ' "If it only puts him in the vein to leave his poor clerk fifty pounds, *that's* something" '
2. For example:

   Fezziwig holds a party for his family, friends, neighbours and employees to celebrate Christmas.

   Scrooge buys the Cratchit family a turkey.
3. A, B, E, F, H, I are all valid.
4. Using both key events and quotations is likely to be the most effective approach.

Page 45

1. All are valid.
2. For example:

   Waking on Christmas morning, Scrooge recognises the importance of kindness and generosity.

   This generosity is in total contrast to the meanness and hard-heartedness he shows at the beginning of the novel.

   This demonstration of kindness and generosity is central to Scrooge's transformation.

   Dickens intends the reader to celebrate Scrooge's transformation and be moved to follow his example of kindness and generosity.

Page 46

uses a key event as evidence	For example, he grudgingly allows Bob Cratchit just one day's holiday at Christmas
uses a quotation as evidence	' "can't afford to make idle people merry" '
explains the context of the evidence	refuses to give money to a gentleman who is collecting for the poor and needy so they can have food and warmth at Christmas.
analysis comment on the writer's choices of language and/or structure	The word 'idle' suggests that Scrooge thinks the poor are poor because they are lazy and will not work.

analysis comment on character	His rejection of this opportunity to be kind and generous shows how hard-hearted and cold Scrooge is,
analysis comment on theme	Scrooge comes to understand the rewards that kindness and generosity can bring.
analysis comment on Dickens' intention	making the reader feel angry and unsympathetic towards him.

Page 48

See the suggested answers for page 40 above.

Unit 7

Page 51

1. For example: Many children in Victorian Britain are suffering from poverty. Society takes no interest in improving this situation, its only remedies being prisons and workhouses to punish them.
2. a … happily celebrating Christmas.

   b … they show the Christmas enjoyed by the wealthy.

   c … they show the Christmas enjoyed by the poor.
3. Scrooge does not celebrate Christmas. Despite his wealth, he lives a life of poverty as he refuses to spend money on any kind of comfort or happiness.

Page 52

1. For example:
   - Beginning: … Scrooge's coldness, meanness and isolation.
   - Middle: … spirits of past, present and future, showing visions of hardship, suffering, generosity and kindness.
   - End: … Scrooge's transformation, kindness and generosity.
2. For example:

   The Ghost of Christmas Past shows Scrooge and the reader the causes of his unhappiness and isolation.

   The Ghost of Christmas Present shows Scrooge and the reader the importance of Christmas, the importance of kindness and generosity, and the contrast of poverty and wealth.

   The Ghost of Christmas Yet To Come shows Scrooge the consequences of his love of money and his isolation.

Page 53

1. a All are valid, although A is a weaker comment without the support of B and C to develop it.
2. Comments are likely to focus on:
   - the contrast of the unhappiness and isolation in Chapter 4 with the images of happy family Christmases in Chapter 3
   - the shocking consequences of Scrooge's actions in life, positioned near the end of the story to prompt Scrooge's transformation.

Page 54

1. The positioning of the appearance of Marley's Ghost at the beginning of the story.

2. Intention: *By positioning Marley's visit at the start of the novel, Dickens makes it clear to Scrooge and to the reader that he will face the same justice if he does not change his ways.*

3. Question: *This helps to engage the reader, but it is also a warning that we should all think about justice and fairness and pay close attention to what the other spirits will show us.*

Page 56

Key events could include:

• Scrooge's love of money and the loss of his fiancée
• Scrooge's isolation, described in Chapter 1
• the choices Scrooge makes in Chapter 1
• the choices Scrooge makes in Chapter 5.

Key structural features could include:

• the pattern of visions that directly contradict and correct Scrooge's choices: for example, his choice to isolate himself contrasted with the happiness he experiences at the visions of Fezziwig's party and his nephew's Christmas celebrations

• Scrooge's choices in Chapter 5 mirroring and contradicting those he makes in Chapter 1: he shows kindness to his employee, Bob Cratchit; he will go to his nephew's for Christmas; he donates to charity.

Unit 8

Page 59

1. All are relevant.

2. Scrooge: Christmas, Industrial Revolution, Charity, Family

   The Cratchits: Family, Industrial Revolution, Poor, Charity

   Ghosts of Christmas: Christmas

   Ignorance and Want: Industrial Revolution, Poor, New Poor Law, Charity

Page 60

1. a) A identifies a relevant attitude.

   B: identifies a relevant attitude; identifies the time in which the novel was written; considers Dickens' intention.

   C: identifies a relevant attitude; identifies the time in which the novel was written; considers Dickens' intention; considers the impact on the reader.

   b) B and C are the most detailed, developed comments on context.

2. Sample responses:

   Dickens is drawing attention to two serious problems that he felt destroyed the lives of poor children in the 1840s.

   The only chance of education they were given was in a charity school but many children had to work and use their wages to help their family survive.

   The only support for the poor who were in 'want' was the workhouse.

   Dickens wants the reader to recognise that the generosity of the wealthier people in society could end these children's suffering.

Page 61

1. a) Sentences A–D focus on impact; sentences a–d focus on context.

   b) c is relevant to A; a is relevant to B; b is relevant to C; d is relevant to D.

   c) Any two combinations from b above would be valid.

Page 62

The most shocking part of the story in which Dickens presents the poor is when the Ghost of Christmas Present shows Scrooge the two children, Ignorance and Want.	uses a key event as evidence
They are described as 'yellow' and 'wolfish',	uses a quotation as evidence
creating a disturbing impression of the poor.	comments on the impact of the evidence
The Ghost makes it clear that Man is responsible, suggesting that the richer people in society have created children like Ignorance and Want by exploiting them, making them work long hours in poor conditions for very little money. Many Victorians blamed the poor for being poor, thinking they were lazy and irresponsible	identifies a relevant contextual point
so this scene highlights Dickens' concern at the way in which the Victorians treated the poor	explores Dickens' intention in the light of this contextual point
and encourages the reader to recognise their responsibility for them and see the importance of giving to charity.	explores the reader's response in the light of this contextual point

Page 64

Responses could focus on:

• Scrooge's stubborn, heartless denial of Christmas spirit, the responsibilities of family and charity in Chapter 1

• points at which Scrooge shows significant change or the willingness to change; for example:
  ○ following Fezziwig's party, he feels he would like to talk to Bob Cratchit
  ○ during the vision of the Cratchits' Christmas, his concern that Tiny Tim should not die
  ○ his recognition that he is similar to the dead man in Chapter 5.

Comments on context could include:

• Victorian attitudes to Christmas
• the importance of family
• the duties of charity.

Unit 9

Page 67

1. For example:

   A cold-hearted, isolated
   B vulnerable, distraught
   C happy, affectionate
   D happy, compassionate

E happy, affectionate

F sympathetic, caring

G anxious, thoughtful

H distraught, repentant

I ecstatic, relieved

J generous, kind

(2) For example:

A surprise, disgust

B concern, sympathy

C surprise, happiness

D happiness, sympathy

E happiness, sympathy

F shock, relief

G sympathy, tension

H tension, sympathy

I relief, laughter

J happiness, admiration

Page 68

(1) **(a)** When, Although, because

(b) All version Bs use conjunctions to express the relationship between the two clauses more clearly.

(2) For example:

<u>When</u> Scrooge sees the Cratchits enjoying Christmas, he asks if Tiny Tim will live.

Scrooge hates Christmas <u>because</u> he thinks it is a waste of money.

Scrooge gradually realises he wants to change, <u>although</u> he only really changes at the end of the novel.

Page 69

(1) For example:

(a) The Ghost of Christmas Yet To Come shows Scrooge his own gravestone, although Scrooge does not know whose it is at first.

(b) The Ghost of Christmas Yet To Come shows Scrooge his own gravestone, making him read the inscription upon it.

(c) The Ghost of Christmas Yet To Come shows Scrooge his own gravestone, which shocks him so much that he decides he must change.

(2) For example:

Scrooge refuses to spend Christmas with his nephew, <u>creating</u> the impression that he sees no value in family life.

Scrooge becomes 'a second father' to Tiny Tim, <u>which shows</u> that he has finally recognised the importance of family life.

Page 70

(1) **(a)/(b)** For example: mean and nasty (cold-hearted, unkind, isolated, uncaring); is (rules, dominates, controls); nothing (not important to, not valued by, of no significance).

(c)/(d) For example:

At the start of the novel Scrooge is presented as <u>cold-hearted</u> and <u>uncaring</u>. He <u>refuses to</u> go to his nephew's for Christmas, <u>saying</u> it is a waste of money. He <u>refuses to</u> give money to charity, <u>saying</u> he cannot afford it. This suggests that it is money that <u>rules</u> Scrooge's life <u>and</u> gives the impression that Christmas and family are <u>of no significance</u> to him.